**POCKET
GOOD
GUIDES**

**BEST
YOGA
CENTRES &
RETREATS**

About the Author

Stafford Whiteaker, bestselling author and former monk, is highly experienced in knowing what you might need if you are looking for new lifestyle values, physical and spiritual fitness, or simply some relaxation.

'Whiteaker's belief in the importance of spiritual harmony and peaceful integration of mind and body is often inspiring and always compelling' – *Daily Express*

BEST YOGA CENTRES & RETREATS

GOOD GUIDES

POCKET GOOD GUIDES

STAFFORD WHITEAKER

RIDER BOOKS

LONDON • SYDNEY • AUCKLAND • JOHANNESBURG

For
Carol Barlow

1 3 5 7 9 10 8 6 4 2

Copyright © 2004 by Stafford Whiteaker

First published in 2004 by Rider, an imprint of Ebury Press, Random House,
20 Vauxhall Bridge Road, London SW1V 2SA

Random House Australia (Pty) Limited
20 Alfred Street, Milsons Point,
Sydney, New South Wales 2061, Australia

Random House New Zealand Limited
18 Poland Road, Glenfield,
Auckland 10, New Zealand

Random House South Africa (Pty) Limited
Endulini, 5A Jubilee Road,
Parktown 2193, South Africa

The Random House Group Limited Reg. No. 954009

Papers used by Rider are natural, recyclable products made from wood grown
in sustainable forests.

Typeset by Palimpsest Book Production Limited, Polmont, Stirlingshire

Printed and bound in Denmark by Nørhaven Paperback A/S, Viborg

A CIP catalogue record for this book is available from the British Library

ISBN 1-8441-3227-7

Contents

Acknowledgements

With thanks to Barbara Bagnall for all her help, and for research to Emma Baddeley, Ros Frecker, Gary Fisher and Ingrid Palairet.

INTRODUCTION

YOGA FOR TODAY

Yoga is a practical way to deal with the stresses and strains of modern life. Originating thousands of years ago, it has been described as the oldest system of personal development in the world. Anyone at any age can practise yoga and you can do it anywhere – the yoga elements of postures, breathing and meditation make this possible because they are so adaptable to the individual.

Attending a regular yoga class helps maintain good general health by improving the efficiency of the body. It tones the muscles, loosens up the joints, helps lessen back stiffness and improves overall physical strength and stamina. But the benefits are not just physical: the ultimate aim of yoga is to unite the body, mind and spirit, and it is the fusion of these three elements of our human nature which has given yoga such long-lasting appeal and made it so popular today.

GETTING STARTED WITH YOGA

There are many yoga classes, clubs and groups throughout Britain and across Europe, held in various venues from health clubs and leisure centres to village and church halls. The great thing about yoga is that you need very little equipment and not a lot of space.

Yoga should always be taught by a qualified, insured instructor. Any equipment used should be safe and appropriate for the activity. Some yoga positions should be modified for those with certain medical conditions such as high blood pressure or problem backs. Students should always discuss any medical condition before enrolling on a course.

Most yoga classes fall under the general heading of Hatha yoga, but there are many other schools and forms such as Iyengar and Ashtanga yoga and lesser-known styles ranging from Kripalu to Bihar. No one can say that one school of yoga is better than another: different methods and yoga systems suit different people. What is important is that you find the right kind of yoga for you.

What should you expect to get out of yoga?

Yoga is a mind, body and spiritual practice. You will be able to achieve the calming of the mind, the relaxation and fitness of the body for better health, and the development of greater spiritual consciousness. This may sound a tall order, but this ancient practice has a history which tells us that all these things are possible through regular and authentic yoga. So the real result should be a more complete wholeness of self.

What skills do you need to practise yoga?

You need no special skills. You can be any age and level of fitness when you start. Yoga is for everyone.

What do you wear to do yoga?

Wear loose comfortable clothing. There is no special uniform or dressing up required.

What do you need to take to your yoga class?

You can take a simple yoga mat if one is not provided. These are inexpensive and your teacher will tell you where they can be purchased. Take a towel and a bottle of water. Try to avoid eating two hours before your yoga class, and do not drink alcohol.

DIFFERENT FORMS OF YOGA

Here are a few of the more common forms of yoga that you might encounter when looking for a course or retreat:

Ashtanga yoga is an aerobic form of yoga with constant flowing movements. It is fast and builds up muscle tone and flexibility, as well as detoxing the body. It is not a yoga form for weak or problem backs.

Bikram yoga involves 24 different postures in a steamy sauna-like environment so your body sweats during the session.

Bikti yoga uses chanting and is highly devotional.

Body balance is a modern term meaning a balance of the physical self in body and mind, achieving calmness and fitness.

Chi Kung or **Qigong** is a traditional Chinese practice over 3,000 years old. The exercises are for strength of body, health and fitness, and healing.

Classical yoga is a modern form based on twelve postures. Movement is the key.

Dance yoga is the use of various yoga movements in a dance and music form.

Dru yoga is yoga of the heart or heart centre (called the Anahata chakra). It involves postures designed to stimulate, activate and awaken the heart both in a physical and spiritual sense.

Hatha yoga is really a generic term applied to most yoga styles. It includes the basics such as breathing, posture and relaxing. A good yoga to begin with.

Iyengar yoga is a structured kind of yoga that uses physical props like ropes and a chair to help or enhance postures. Detail is important and there is a strong remedial element in the teaching.

Jnana yoga uses many-faceted meditation in order to find the path of wisdom.

Karma yoga is 'to do' and 'to be' because it is based on the principle that the universe exists in a state of 'cause and effect'. So doing something is 'cause' and the result is 'effect'.

Kripalu yoga is a physical and spiritual concept where all senses are uniquely combined for withdrawal into the inner self, so that the total being is combined into one unity.

Kriya yoga is a practice to gain knowledge of self through breathing.

Kundalini yoga is a form of yoga in which the hidden energy at the bottom of the spine is awakened. Chanting, visualisation, deep breathing and sound are all used. If you are anxious or depressive do not start with this form of yoga.

Mantra yoga is yoga in which you chant or say words, phrases or even just syllables until the mind and emotions are transcended. A typical Tibetan Buddhist mantra might be 'Aum Mani Padme Hum', which means 'The jewel is in the lotus' or a typical Hindu mantra is 'Asato Ma Sat Gamayo', which means 'Lead me from the unreal to the real'.

Neti-Neti yoga is a yoga that discards whatever thoughts or distractions are not an expression of the inner self. So you practise a philosophy and meditation of *neti-neti* or *not this, not that.*

Nidra yoga is deep relaxation yoga at a profound physical and emotional level.

Power Chi is a current modern fitness practice which combines various elements of different systems, mainly t'ai chi and Hatha yoga.

Qigong – See Chi Kung.

Raja yoga is yoga of the mind. It is based on directing one's life force to the highest spiritual goals.

Sadhana means self-realisation and enlightment, the cultivation of self-knowledge and oneness with the universe. So Sadhana yoga focuses on self-realisation as a goal of the yoga practice and teachings.

Satyananda yoga uses various body-and-mind-focusing practices, which lead to deep relaxation and calmness of mind. The main emphasis is on inner awareness.

Shadow yoga is an invigorating and balancing yoga.

Shakti yoga practice has existed for over 1,500 years. It is in the tantric tradition of Hindu spirituality and uses sacred sounds.

Sivananda Hatha yoga is based around twelve positions. Meditation is important.

T'ai chi is the ancient Chinese art of the practice of relaxing movements which give deep balancing of mind and body. The exercises are suitable for every age and person. They are fluid in motion, achieving an equally fluid state of mind and body. T'ai chi not only relaxes the body but tones it up and is practised by millions of people to achieve fitness and good health.

Yogalates – Yogalates is a practice in which the teaching combines movements and elements from both yoga and pilates.

FOUR POINTS OF YOGA

Asana is proper exercise. It acts as a liberating routine for the body, increasing circulation, flexibility and promoting good health. Asanas are at the same time mental exercises in concentration and meditation which produce inner healing.

Pranayama is proper breathing. This connects the whole body to the solar plexus or centre where potential energy is stored. Yoga breathing techniques release this energy for physical and mental wellbeing.

Savasan is proper relaxation. Yoga teaches three levels of relaxation: physical, mental and spiritual.

Vedanta and **Dhyana** are positive thinking and meditation. These two yoga elements relieve stress and restore energy. Meditation improves concentration and brings peace of mind.

MEDITATION

Most students often forget that yoga is a way to awaken the spiritual, and they rarely get beyond learning the various physical movements. Of course, in themselves these are good for you, but meditation is an integral part of yoga. Its purpose is to move us forward in our search for the vision of the hidden self.

The most immediate benefit of any meditation should be that you feel more calm and relaxed. It is an excellent way of combating stress. It should increase your ability to concentrate and generate a sense of a calm centre from which you may direct more of your energy into living more creatively and using your personal talents and gifts. So the true purpose of meditation is to raise the level of your consciousness to the realm of the spiritual. It is crucial to remember that yoga is a practice that involves all three spheres of being: the body, mind and spirit.

HEALING WITH YOGA

The health benefits of regular yoga practice, particularly for those suffering from stress, are well established. Many people, including those in the medical establishment, still view yoga as simply a form of physical exercise and fail to grasp the psychological and more significant physiological benefits. But progress is made all the time and as yoga classes sweep the country, the best testimony to the health benefits will be the improved wellbeing of all these new yoga practitioners.

Many common physical ailments, even some chronic problems, can be improved through regular yoga practice. However, if you have a particular medical condition or are pregnant, you should check with the teacher for guidance before you decide to enrol in the class. If there is any doubt, leave it for a while and think about it again when you are feeling better. That said, yoga has proven to be a healing form of therapy for many health complaints. It tones up the whole person – mind, body and spirit.

Yogabeats *David Sye, The Third Space, 13 Sherwood St, London W1F Tel: 020 7439 6333 www.thirdspace.com*
A fusion of yoga forms and styles by David Sye, who works at different venues. Check out where he is holding classes. He uses music and sound with yoga.

Yogasthma *US Yoga Association, 2159 Filbert St,*
San Francisco, CA 94123, US.
'Seven steps to asthma control for children with asthma and their parents.'

Many traditional medical establishments, including the San Francisco Asthma Task Force and St Luke's Hospital in San Francisco, have been using yoga to treat asthma in both adults and children. Yogasthma is an asthma management programme which focuses on awareness of your asthma condition, proper breathing, how and when to take your medications, achieving a proper balanced diet, living in clean personal space, learning to relax, and taking moderate yoga exercise every day to stretch and strengthen your lungs.

When you consider the emphasis put on breathing in yoga practices, then it is obvious that yoga has a part to play in helping asthmatics. Indeed, recent research has pinpointed incorrect breathing as part of the problem. Yoga as a regular practice also destresses and helps relaxation and this too can have benefits to asthma sufferers. Further information is available through the websites and links of both St Luke's and the San Francisco Asthma Task Force.

Yoga for Health Foundation *Ickwell Bury, Biggleswade, Bedfordshire SG18. Tel: 01767 627271 www.yogaforhealth foundation.co.uk*
This is a special retreat for those who have health problems and disabilities of various kinds as well as for the healthy – no division is made between the fit and the severely disabled, and everyone is well regarded and given loving care by the staff. We were very impressed by the friendly atmosphere of this well-established centre. Yoga training and other healing treatments are available. This is a place where people share and grow in strength together. The health benefits of regu-

lar yoga practice, particularly for those suffering from stress, are well established. The foundation, a charity operating in many parts of the world, is in what must be the last unspoiled bit of this commuter-belt county. A seventeenth-century grand manor and farm, it is surrounded by parkland and fine gardens, and there's a fishing lake left over from the Middle Ages when an abbey occupied the site. Inside the house all is given over to creating a sense of family, and the atmosphere is busy, caring and helpful. The food is excellent with much that is home-produced. There are nursing staff and the place is well equipped for the disabled. On any visit here you are likely to encounter people who will praise the improvements in their lives that stays here have brought them. Meditation room, small conferences, camping by arrangement, garden, library, guest lounge, payphone. Pets by prior agreement. Children welcomed. Full range of yoga activities for both able-bodied and disabled guests. Send for programme of events, which includes a ten-day Family Festival of Yoga.

Chekira Wholistic Trust *Yoga & Therapy Centre,*
Beech Lawn, Beech Grove, Mayford, Woking,
Surrey GU22. Tel: 01483 870064

The Chekira Wholistic Trust is a training centre for the Friends of Yoga Society International and is affiliated to the Institute for Complementary Medicine. The Society was founded in 1970 by the Late Wilfred Clarke who also founded the British Wheel of Yoga. The Trust provides teacher-training courses, teacher supply and support, weekend yoga workshops, weekly yoga classes, private one-to-one tuition, and certain complementary therapies. The director of the Chekira Trust is Brenda Brown, who has been teaching yoga for over 30 years. She and her team of qualified yoga teachers and

therapists work throughout Surrey and the surrounding areas.
Yoga with Josephine *Ludshott House, Grayshott, Surrey GU26 6DR. Tel: 01428 604898 jchiover@aol.com*
One-to-one yoga sessions only. Specialises in yoga for asthma and lower back problems.
Royal London Homeopathic Hospital *Greenwell St, London W1W. Tel: 020 7391 8833 hamish@astangayoga.co.uk www.astangayoga.co.uk*

YOGA FOR KIDS

Yoga is a great activity for children because it is an expressive art and not just a contemplative exercise. However, qualified teachers are an absolute essential when children are involved, and it's crucial that teachers really care about kids and have plenty of enthusiasm. Yoga is often helpful with children who need to build up general body strength and balance or need a greater expansion of the lungs for breathing. If you want to start your child in a yoga class, always visit the centre first, ask about the teacher's qualifications and watch one of the children's yoga classes. You will soon see how much the kids enjoy this ancient art.

Unfortunately, you may not be able to find a class near you, but expect yoga for kids to be a growth area around the country. If you cannot get to the following places in London, check out your local facilities regularly to see what is being offered. If none are yet available, perhaps you could suggest to your yoga teacher that there should be a class for kids too (but remember the teacher must be trained to work with children). At the moment so many activities are on offer in local public and private centres and clubs for children that yoga has not yet made inroads into most activity programmes – but the future looks bright.

Art of Health & Yoga Centre 208 Balham High Street, London SW17. Tel: 020 8682 1800 www.artofhealth.co.uk
This centre has pioneered a new approach to yoga for kids, especially the younger ones. The class is called Yoga Bugs and is for three- to seven-year-olds. More than 100 teachers have been trained so far and there are nine locations around Balham, Tooting and Clapham. There are also Yoga Children classes for the eight- to twelve-year-olds.

Holistic Health 64 Broadway Market, London E8.
Tel: 020 7275 8434 www.holistic-health-hackney.co.uk
Yoga for kids aged three to six.

Iyengar Institute 223A Randolph Avenue, London W9.
Tel: 020 7624 3080 www.iyi.org.uk
A class for seven- to fourteen-year-olds and one for teenagers, but Iyengar yoga, in its strict and pure form, is not suitable for younger children.

Kilburn Yoga Centre First Floor, 332 Kilburn High Road, London NW6. Tel: 020 7624 1804
Gentle, relaxing and small classes in a modest but nice place. Baby massage is also available.

Sivananda Yoga Vedanta Centre 51 Felsham Road, London SW15. Tel: 020 8780 0160 www.sivanandayoga.org/london
Children's classes are held once a week on a Sunday. Go along and watch a class, get to know the people, then take along your child to see how it goes.

Triyoga 6 Erskine Road, London NW3. Tel: 020 7483 3344 www.triyoga.co.uk
Twice-weekly children's yoga classes, catering for six- to ten-year-olds and over elevens. Not expensive. Large centre dedicated to yoga.

Yoga Therapy Centre 90–92 Pentonville Road, London N1.
Tel: 020 7689 3040 www.yogatherapy.org

You can bring your baby here from birth to two years old to enjoy a parent and baby class. There are also special yoga classes for asthmatic children. Go along and discuss it.

YOGA & PREGNANCY

Relaxation, toning and stretching muscles that you will need during the birthing process, and building up stamina, are important aspects of yoga in pregnancy. Attending a group class with other expectant mothers will also help your confidence and can be fun. Yoga practice after giving birth will help restore muscle tone and get you back into shape quicker.

If you decide to take up yoga while pregnant, you must attend a yoga class specifically designed for pregnant women with a teacher who is qualified in applying yoga practices for pregnancy. If in any doubt do not enrol in the class. Here are some basic guidelines:

• Do not attend a regular yoga class but enrol in one for prenatal or postnatal women.
• Do make certain your teacher is a qualified yoga teacher and experienced in teaching pregnant women.
• Do tell your doctor that you are considering going to a yoga class so this may be noted on your medical records.

We believe that the teacher should always be a woman and preferably a mother herself so that she has a profound understanding of pregnancy and birth at every level, whether that be mental, physical or spiritual.

There are a number of books about pregnancy and yoga that demonstrate how yoga can help you. They guide the prospective mother through the experience, advising on how to be happy and relaxed during pregnancy, how to prepare for birth and how to get back to fitness after the baby is born. The following books are particularly helpful:

Francoise Barbira Freedman, *Yoga for Pregnancy*, Cassell, 1998

Roslind Widdowson, *Yoga for Pregnancy*, Hamlyn, 2001

Sandra Sabatini, *Preparing for Birth with Yoga*, HarperCollins, 1994

Francoise Barbira Freedman, *Postnatal Yoga*, Lorenz Books, 2000

There are a growing number of qualified yoga teachers in Britain who are offering classes in yoga during pregnancy. Among these is Sarah March D'Angelo, who includes in her Hatha yoga approach an emphasis on the spiritual preparation and awareness of the whole process of pregnancy and birth.

YOGA ACTIVITIES

There are yoga classes, courses, weekends and retreats.

Classes are usually once a week and each session lasts from about an hour to an hour and a half. You usually sign up for a few months, half a year or a full year. In some classes you simply drop in and pay without having to enrol first or pay for future sessions.

The course may focus on a specific yoga system like Hatha, and can be specially designed to cover only certain aspects of yoga practice, such as meditation.

Weekend courses are usually from Friday to Sunday and have a programme of yoga sessions combined with other group activities and time given to talks and periods of relaxation. These will have a set fee and may or may not include accommodation and food.

Retreats can be near home or on distant shores, for a weekend, a week or much longer. Yoga retreats almost always contain the holiday element so that you get plenty of rest, relaxation and fun as well as lots of yoga teaching and practice. A yoga retreat is an excellent and healthy way to increase fitness and get an emotional detox.

USING THIS BOOK

The book is organised around where the yoga centre, retreat or course is held. Where the yoga place, school association or their work covers a whole county or country then the name is given at the beginning of that section.

For England, the listing starts with London, which is organised according to the postcode. After London, yoga places are organised by the region of the country, for example *South*, then by the county, for example *Sussex*, and then in alphabetical order by the town or village. The places within the town or village where the yoga is held are then given in alpabetical order, with address and telephone number. Email addresses and websites are given where applicable.

Information about the place is given when we thought it would be helpful. Please bear in mind that both teachers and classes on offer change frequently so you always need to check out what is on before going along to a class or course.

In some cases the full address of a teacher or contact is not given. This is because the person involved does not teach or work at home and their personal address is therefore private and irrelevant to your enquiry.

For Scotland the same method of listing is used. For Wales the listing is by town or city.

For France, the listing begins with *General France* if the yoga place or association applies to yoga throughout France, such as *La Fédération Nationale des Enseignants de Yoga* (*F.N.E.Y.*). Following these initial listings, the name of the department is given: for example *Creuse*, then the actual place, *La Cellette*, and then the name of the place, *Le Blé en Herbe*, with its address and contact information.

For other countries such as Spain or Greece, the places are listed according to region or area, such as *Granada* or *Paros*. If there is more than one yoga place in that area or town, then these are organised alphabetically.

LONDON

In London, if you want yoga, you get yoga. Yoga classes and instruction abound, probably just around the corner from where you live or work. They range from ones which can be found in local authority centres, usually professionally run by private companies, where any fees involved are fairly modest, to private clubs and centres where facilities can be top of the range with prices to match. There are classes and courses in special yoga centres, dance studios, gyms, alternative therapy centres, health associations, church halls and private homes. In fact, just about any place where people can practise yoga and chill out.

But be warned – classes in central London get filled up quickly, particularly at the end of the normal working day.

Always at the heart of things, London has a number of yoga centres devoted to specific types of yoga, such as Hatha or Iyengar yoga.

Yoga for children in London

When it comes to the kids, London offers yoga classes for all ages, from babies to teens, which outside London is hard to find. **As always, make sure teachers are qualified. When it comes to children, teachers should have special qualifications for understanding the physical and emotional demands of this age group.** Yoga is fun for your kids and it gives them a system of self-practice for balanced health that can be used all their lives.

How to use the London section

The London section is organised as follows. First you will find a **London General** section, which details various yoga centres and teaching associations from which you may obtain more specific information about classes and courses. After this comes the **list of places** where you will find yoga classes. These are organised according to the postcode. For example, a place with a SW10 postcode would be listed under the London South-West section, while a place with a WC1 postcode would be found under London West Central. Finally, there is a list of major players in the private health clubs business who frequently include yoga in their programmes.

LONDON GENERAL

Art of Health & Yoga Centre *Tel: 020 8682 1800* Contact Robert Lindsell

City Yoga Centre *Tel: 020 7253 3000* Contact Paul Lurenson

Community Yoga Centre *Tel: 020 7690 8139 yoga@cwcom.net*

Complete Health Care Centre *Tel: 020 7336 0466 www.completehealthcare.co.uk* Bright and welcoming centre designed to make you feel well and relaxed.

Hatha Yoga for Body–Mind Awareness *Tel: 020 7372 2203* Contact Maro Stoyanuidou

Hatha Yoga Classes in London *www.gymuser.org.uk/yoga*

Islington Yoga *www.islingtonyoga.com* Islington Yoga has been going for some time and the reason there is not an address is because the teachers, John Evans and Karen Watson, hold classes at different venues in Islington. So go to their website for details of their programme and current London class venues.

London Road Yoga *www.londonroadyoga.com* Tasha Diamant and Robert McClelland are the founders of London Road Yoga.

Maida Vale Yoga Institute – Iyengar Yoga *Tel: 020 7624 3080* Contact Rosanne Seal

New River Sports Centre *www.haringeyleisure.com* A serious workout and get-fit place. Yoga classes are held here.

North-East London Iyengar Yoga Institute *Tel: 020 7256 49137* Contact Brigid Philip

Portobello Green Fitness Centre *Tel: 020 8960 2221* Yoga with Marc Ansari

Practical Ayurveda *27 Lankers Drive, North Harrow, London HA2* Contact Dr Anne Roden by letter

Rachel Barrance Hatha Yoga *Tel: 07789 881205 netrnb@breathemail.net*

School of Yoga *Westminster & Croydon. Tel: 020 8657 3258*

Spring Health Leisure Club *Tel: 020 7483 6800 www.springhealthleisure.com* Modern, clean, light and airy and very popular with women. Bring the baby because there's a crèche with trained nannies. Many different types of yoga on offer. Smart.

Sitaram Partnership *Tel: 020 8678 0054 www.sitaram.org* The therapeutic application of yoga in a private residence where there is a yoga room set aside. Individual sessions available. For most people a group is the best way to begin yoga because you get personal guidance, the chance to observe others, and support from the group, which can be fun – but for others a kick-start with one-to-one tuition may prove right.

Toynbee Hall *Tel: 01255 551443* Contact Peter Ballard

Yoga Mosaic Association of Jewish yoga teachers *www.yogamosaic.org*

Yoga Shakti Mission London *www.yogashakti.org/london*

Viniyoga *Tel: 01304 367166* Contact Pamela Tyson

Viniyoga South London *Tel: 020 7708 5636* Contact Geoff Farrer

LONDON NORTH

Amazon Fitness *134 Stoke Newington Church Street, London N16. Tel: 020 7241 1449* A small women-only gym and studio. Some healing and relaxation therapies on offer, as well as yoga in a nicely planned programme of courses.

Bob Breen Academy *20 Hoxton Square, London N1. Tel: 020 7729 5789 www.bobbreen.co.uk* An internationally known centre for the martial arts with a younger client membership, this place knows its stuff and among the classes on offer is yoga. Why not add boxing to your schedule?

Clissold Leisure Centre *63 Clissold Road, London N16. Tel: 020 7275 2950* A glass and steel construction, this big place has loads on offer with a multi-tiered membership rate. Check out the 88 pieces of gym stuff, plunge in the pool, join the yoga class. Bar. Café. Crèche.

Compton Sports Centre *Sunny Way, Summers Lane, London N12. Tel: 020 8361 8658* This is a good bet. Airy and full of light, you can use the sauna or have a swim after your yoga workout. Well-trained staff.

Factory *407 Hornsey Road, London N19. Tel: 020 7272 1122 www.tangolondon.com* Relaxed place much favoured by women. Well-known dance venue. Yoga is usually on offer.

Nataraja Yoga Centre *46 Crouch Hall Road, London N8. Tel: 020 8340 5279*

Peak Fitness *262 Green Lanes, London N13. Tel: 020 8882 9102 www.peak-fitness.co.uk* A welcoming, modern place, popular with women.

Rowans Health & Fitness Club *10 Stroud Green Road, London N4. Tel: 020 8211 7766 www.rowans.co.uk* Once upon a time this was a big cinema but now it's a modern health club where among other classes, yoga is on offer. There are still lingering reminders of its heyday as a flick house which is rather fun. Just across the street from Finsbury Park station.

Southgate Leisure Centre *Winchmore Hill Road, London N14. Tel: 020 8882 7963* Dance and yoga studio in one of the most modern local leisure places.

Space *Hackney Community College, Shoreditch Campus, Falkirk Street, London N1. Tel: 020 7613 9123* A new sports and performing arts complex. Singles and families both well catered for here. Loads of good facilities on offer including courses and classes in dance, martial arts, pilates, fitness and yoga.

Sunstone Health & Leisure Club for Women *16 Northwold Road, London N16. Tel: 020 7923 1991 www.sunstonewomen.com* Three floors of luxury exercise and wellbeing available here in what used to be a church. Crèche available. Lots of facilities and classes, including yoga.

Yoga Therapy Centre *Yoga Biomedical Trust, 90–92 Pentonville Road, London N1. Tel: 020 7689 3040. www.yogatherapy.org* Founded by Dr Robin Monro in 1983, this is a well-known establishment for using yoga therapeutically. Expert assessments are part of the consultations.

Yoga for Gay Men *255 Liverpool Road, London N1. Tel: 020 7625 4521 www.gn.apc.org/gayyoga* David Tierney holds weekly classes including one for beginners.

Yoga Junction *97 Seven Sisters Road, London N7. Tel: 020 7263 3113 info@yogajunction.com www.yogajunction.com* Hatha and Ashtanga yoga classes.

Yoga with Veronika *49 Pemberton Road, London N4. Tel: 0208 352 2657/07799 532826 veronikapenadere@hotmail.com* Veronika Pena de la Jara teaches Hatha yoga and traditional classes in London and Reading. She takes a lot of classes and is well known in local yoga circles. Contact her for details and discuss what would suit you.

LONDON NORTH-WEST

Air Studios *Top Floor, 6A Crane Grove, London NW2. Tel: 020 8493 1486.* Teacher Nigel Jones gives 'Talk Through Primary Yoga' courses, drop-in classes on a Saturday, introduction courses to Astanga yoga, and a regular beginners class.

Bikram Yoga College of India *173 Queens Crescent, London NW5. Tel: 020 8692 6900 www.bikramyoga.co.uk* Strip down to shorts, get into the yoga that Hollywood made famous, and start sweating. Qualified teachers and regular yoga classes during the day. Heat up and lift your spirits. Classes of the Bikram form only. Friendly staff.

Brunswick Health & Fitness *311B Chase Road, London N14. Tel: 020 8886 9111* Not much to look at from the outside but inside all is OK with good facilities and classes.

The Circle Health Club *41 Mackennal Street, London NW8. Tel: 020 7722 1234 www.circlehealthclub.co.uk* A warm welcome here. Good staff and facilities. Regular yoga classes.

Diorama 2 *3–7 Euston Centre, Regents Place, London NW1. Tel: 020 7916 5467 www.diorama-arts.org.uk* Right in the middle of London. Good atmosphere, lots of attention for beginners. Dynamic classes. Mixed crowd.

Fluid Form *Tony Susnjara & Christina Paternas, 9 Sharpleshall Street, London NW1. Tel: 020 7586 1203 info@fluidformyoga.com www.fluidformyoga.com* This organisation has courses and workshops in Fluid Form and Hatha yoga and provides yoga venues in different sites, mainly in London, with a wide-ranging timetable available.

Hamish Hendry at Ashtanga Place Diorama 1 *34 Osnaburgh Street, London NW1. Tel: 020 8342 9762 www. ashtangayoga.co.uk* Hamish Hendry is one of the best known and most respected teachers of this form of yoga. This is a plain, down-to-earth, no-frills place. You come to do your yoga. You learn what yoga is supposed to be about. Go authentic yoga, go here.

Hendon Youth Sports Centre *Marble Drive, London NW2. Tel: 020 8455 0818 www.barnet.gov.uk* Don't let the name put you off – you don't have to be a youth to enjoy going here. Impressive range of training equipment and known for its extensive gymnastics facilities, this is a modern place with a wide choice of classes on offer.

Jubilee Hall *25 Pond Street, London NW3. Tel: 020 7431 2263 www.jubileehallclubs.co.uk* Yoga classes are held in an attic studio that works OK with light from big windows. This place is not top of the list at the moment but staff are friendly.

Kilburn Yoga Room *First Floor, 332 Kilburn High Street, London NW6. Tel: 020 7624 1804* Local and affordable yoga. Relaxed, simple place. Some yoga workshops as well as regular classes.

Manor Health & Leisure *307 Cricklewood Broadway, London NW2. Tel: 020 8450 6464 www.themanorfitness.co.uk* Space, space and more space in this made-over residential place. Good value for your money and in addition to yoga there are mind, body and soul sessions as well as the usual fitness stuff.

Soho Gym *193 Camden High Street, London NW1. Tel: 020 7482 4524 www.sohogyms.co.uk* From internet café to personal trainers, here is the place. Big, best, classy are all words that spring to mind . . . and the yoga instruction is good. Popular with women and a cheerful place for all.

Swanfleet Centre *93 Fortess Road, London NW5. Tel: 020 7267 9465 www.geocities.com/hatha yoga*

Triyoga *6 Erskine Road, London NW3. Tel: 020 7483 3344*

Willesden Sports Centre *Donnington Road, London NW10. Tel: 020 8459 6605* Outdoor and indoor activities plus a pool.

Light and airy exercise rooms but you won't want to linger in the changing rooms. Café.

London West Central

Central YMCA Club *112 Great Russell Street, London WC1B. Tel: 020 7343 1700 theclub@centralymca.org.uk www.central ymca.org.uk/club Time Out* gave this place a great vote: 'There's nowhere in London that can beat the unpretentious atmosphere and broad curriculum of this huge but friendly club.' High praise indeed and justified. It is large and friendly, like an over-sized teddy bear, with loads of activities – aqua, weight management, holistic, pamper and kids are all words that describe activities and classes on offer. Translate these as swimming, gym and exercise, yoga and related classes, alternative healing therapies, crèche, holiday and after-school activities for the gang. Hatha and Power yoga are both on offer with several classes held each week. There is also a yoga induction class, to give beginners an opportunity to learn techniques and get the hang of it. The YMCA gives a neat definition of its yoga classes: 'A controlled movement class aiding relaxation and stress management with flexibility bene-fits.' Who could say no? Fees for joining the Central YMCA include those for both weekly and annual memberships with a one-day taster membership at about £15.

Jubilee Hall *30 The Piazza, London WC2. Tel: 020 7836 4007 www.jubileehallclubs.co.uk* Top-range prices, rather elite crowd, super environment, good lighting.

The Locomotion Fitness & Leisure Club *Holiday Inn, 1 Kings Cross Road, London WC1. Tel: 020 7837 0115* This is a small gym and pool under the Holiday Inn, not much used by hotel guests. No personal trainers but gym instruction is available. They are developing a programme of classes but yoga is on offer already. Clean and welcoming.

Natural Health Centre *46 Theobalds Road, London WC1. Tel: 020 7242 7080* Small building, some therapies. A so-so place. Yoga on offer.

Royal London Homeopathic Hospital *Greenwell St, London W1W. Tel: 020 7391 8833/020 7700 3710 hamish@Ashtangayoga.co.uk www.ashtangayoga.co.uk*

Soho Gym *12 Macklin Street, London WC2. Tel: 020 7242 1290 www.sohogyms.co.uk* Various yoga disciplines on offer. Mostly men working out. Bodies beautiful is the name of the game here.

Yoga Place *The Peel Centre, Percy Circus, London WC1. Tel: 020 7833 0422 Vitality_uk@hotmail.com*

Yoga Therapy Centre *Royal London Homeopathic Hospital, Greenwell St, London W1W. Tel: 020 7391 8833 vinyasayoga@yahoo.com www.ashtangayoga.co.uk* Yoga with Cathy Louise Broda. Ring the hospital for yoga therapy information.

LONDON WEST

Agua at Sanderson *50 Berners Street, London W1. Tel: 020 7300 1414* Extraordinary high design or high camp place, depending on your taste. Mirrors, mirrors everywhere. Great staff, giving the place true quality. Not crowded. Relax in splendour and do your yoga too.

Bikram Yoga Centre *260 Kilburn Lane, London W10. Tel: 020 8960 9644 www.bikramyoga.co.uk* Be reminded that Bikram yoga is practised in humid, sauna-like conditions to relax the muscles. If you don't like getting heated up this is not the place for you. But this form of yoga is celebrity liked, especially in the States. Nice place to work up your yoga… and your sweat. Café. Shop.

Bliss *333 Portobello Road, London W10. Tel: 020 8969 3331* *www.bliss.me.co.uk* Clinic, shop and café, plus yoga and yoga massage.

Broadway Squash & Fitness Centre *Chalk Hill Road, London W6. Tel: 020 8741 4640* You'll find this place under the Novotel Hotel in Hammersmith. Clean, smart and well used. Friendly gym and squash courts. Yoga on regular offer.

Champneys Piccadilly *21A Piccadilly, London W1. Tel: 020 7255 8000 www.champneys.com* Pool, beauty therapy, martial arts, weights room, music to work out to, pilates, yoga. Spacious place.

Charing Cross Sports Centre *Aspenlea Road, Hammersmith, London W6. Tel: 020 8741 3654 www.ccsclub. co.uk* Impressive pool and facilities. A good health and fitness place. Regular yoga classes. Bar.

Club Kensington *201–207 Kensington High Street, London W8 Tel: 020 7937 5386 www.clubkensington.com* One of London's oldest clubs but has been revised and updated. Yoga usually on offer.

Danceworks *16 Balderton Street, London W1. Tel: 020 7629 6183 www.danceworks.co.uk* Find the Selfridges clock and walk up the little street directly opposite and before you know it you'll be in Danceworks, with its six studios and running programme of more than 160 classes every week. The atmosphere is sparkling, with people getting on with bodywork in all manner of ways. Ages range up to the senior citizen, who is likely to be trim and fit and working out at the ballet bar, but in general there's a young crowd here. The place gets very busy after normal working hours. Yoga on offer includes Ashtanga yoga, classical yoga, dance-based yoga, Hatha yoga, Kundalini yoga and Opening The Shadow (Shadow yoga founded by Shandor Remete), an invigorating and balancing sequence yoga especially good for beginners. In addition, there are three yoga-based courses: Pilates Mat Work, for core control and strengthening back and abdominal muscles, Yogaworks, which springs from both yoga and Feldenkrais techniques, and Yogamonks, which is a blend of Vinyasa yoga and pilates to invigorate and align the body. The studios used for yoga are all very light and clean. In addition to clean changing rooms and showers, the facilities include an internet café and an alternative therapy centre. The Natureworks holistic health centre offers massage and bodywork, dance injury treatment and other body-related therapies like aura imaging and health kinesiology. Dancework fees are in a broad band, ranging from about £120 for annual membership to £4 for a yoga class.

Gold's Gym *54–62 Uxbridge Road, London W7. Tel: 020 8840 0044* General health and fitness place with good facilities. Great changing rooms with their own steam rooms and saunas. Crèche. Parking. Background music to exercise to. OK place for yoga.

Gurnell Leisure Centre *Ruislip Road East, London W13. Tel: 020 8998 3241 www.leisureconnection.co.uk* Big pool. Popular place. Good facilities. Regular yoga and other worthwhile classes.

Hale Clinic *7 Park Crescent, London W1. Tel: 020 7631 0156 www.haleclinic.com* Integrates conventional and complementary medicine.

Himalayan International Institute of Yoga Science & Philosophy *70 Claremont Road, London W13. Tel: 020 8997 3544*

Hogarth Health Club *Airedale Avenue, London W4. Tel: 020 8995 4600* Luxury sums it up. Everything you could wish for in a club and very smart to boot. Bar. Crèche.

Innergy Yoga Centre *Acorn Hall, East Row, Kensal Road,*

London W10. Tel: 020 8968 1178 www.innergy-yoga.com This
is a serious place for yoga. Regular classes in which you will
come to appreciate the true nature of yoga. This place is not
about fashion and trendy surroundings but about taking yoga
as a potentially life-forming and life-changing practice. What
a refreshing change. Go and try it.

Inspiration *Westbourne Studios, 242 Acklam Road, London
W10. Tel: 020 7229 3384* Small classes, trendy operation,
qualified teachers. Gallery. Café. Regular yoga.

Iyengar Yoga Institute Maida Vale *223a Randolph Avenue,
Maida Vale, London W9. Tel: 020 7624 3080 office@iyi.org.uk
www.iyi.org.uk* The largest purpose-built yoga centre in
Europe. Set back from the road, the centre is quiet and nestles
in a leafy garden. The simple design of the place affords plenty
of natural sunlight – and white walls, under-floor heating and
two large airy studios make for a formal but comfortable yoga
centre. Clarity, control and peace are the key words here,
and there is attention to detail and focus on proper align-
ment. There are daily classes for students of varying abilities.
These include foundation courses for beginners, general,
intermediate, 59+ classes, children, pregnancy, remedial and
Pranayama. There are special workshops, lectures, demonstrations and teacher-training courses also available. Teachers
visit from India and other international centres on a regular
basis. Everyone is welcome but membership is obligatory
after the second visit. Nearest tube: Maida Vale.

Janet Adegoke Leisure Centre *Bloemfontein Road, London
W12. Tel: 020 8743 3401* Family-orientated centre with swimming pools. Big programme of classes and courses on offer
including yoga. Sports hall. Crèche.

Jubilee Sports Centre *Caird Street, London W10. Tel: 020
8960 9629 www.courtneys.co.uk* State-of-the-art place with

loads of light. Yoga and much more besides. Worth your time.
Ladbroke Rooms *8 Telford Road, London W10. Tel: 020 8960 0846 www.theladbrokerooms.com* Impressive range of therapies and activities on offer, including yoga.

Lambton Place Health Club *Lambton Place, London W11. Tel: 020 7229 2291 www.hogarthgroup.co.uk* Comfortable place. Training and yoga offered. Intimate studio. Qualified staff. Internet and coffee area.

The Life Centre *15 Edge Street, London W8 7PN. Tel: 020 7221 4602 www.thelifecentre.org* Contact Godfrey Devereaux. Open seven days a week with a dedicated team, the Life Centre has been going since 1993. It is a non-membership place that tries to be a one-stop health and fitness centre, combining over 50 hours of classes each week with a complementary therapy clinic. There is a special programme of teachers and events each year, some in different venues or outside London. Recent examples are Cathy Louise Broda for Mysore yoga practice, David Williams giving an Ashtanga yoga workshop and the American teacher Rod Stryker leading a workshop intensive in Somerset. Yoga classes for kids aged five to eleven are also regularly held. A calm place in a former church.

Masbro Centre *87 Masbro Road, London W14. Tel: 020 7605 0800* Friendly place. Regular yoga classes.

Moberly Sports & Education Centre *Kilburn Lane, London W10. Tel: 020 7641 4807* More than just a gym and sports annex to the local school. Popular place, with women-only evenings.

Next Generation Carlton Club *1 Alfred Road, London W2. Tel: 020 7266 9300 www.nextgenerationclubs.co.uk* Part of a chain of clubs. All ages and abilities welcomed. Separate kids' facility. Dance and yoga studio.

Paddington Recreation Ground *Randolph Avenue, London*

W9. Tel: 020 7641 3642 www.courtneys.co.uk Home of the Japan Karate Association, this is a grand place full of facilities and activities. Spoiled for choice here.

The Park Club *East Acton Lane, London W3. Tel: 020 8743 4321 www.hogarthgroup.co.uk* Beauty salon, dance studios, sauna, swimming pool, spa and more, including yoga classes.

The Phillimore Club *45 Phillimore Walk, London W8. Tel: 020 7937 2882 www.phillimoreclub.com* An underground oasis of looking and feeling better. Women only. Regular yoga.

Portobello Green Fitness Club *3–5 Thorpe Close, London W10. Tel: 020 8960 2221* Cosmopolitan. Buzzy. Music plus yoga and the lot. Down-to-earth. Have some yoga, have some fun!

Relaxation Centre *7–11 Kensington High Street, London W8. Tel: 020 7938 3409*

Shared Experience Yoga Group *Oxford Circus, London W1. Tel: 020 8858 7286* Contact J. Friedeberger

Shivashack *31B Churchfield Road, London W3. Tel: 020 8993 3399* Recently established basement venue. Regular yoga classes plus remedial yoga. Youngish crowd. 25 maximum to a class.

Spirit Health Club *Posthouse Hotel Kensington, Wrights Lane, London W8. Tel: 020 7368 4005* Spotless place. Polite staff and a genteel atmosphere in which to pursue your yoga.

Sport Dimension *9 Wilson Walk, Prebend Gardens, London W4. Tel: 020 8563 0007* Underneath the station arches. Peaceful, spacious place with good equipment and programme.

Tabernacle Trust *Powis Square, London W11. Tel: 020 7565 7890 www.tabernacle.org.uk* Well-known yoga teachers in a former church. A good place to begin or continue your yoga practice.

Third Space *13 Sherwood Street, London W1. Tel: 020 7439 6333 www.thirdspace.com* Everything you could want in the way of facilities. Fantastic choice.

Twyford Sports Centre *Twyford Crescent, London W3. Tel: 020 8993 9095* In the grounds of a local school, so only open to the public after 6pm. Facilities geared towards the recreational but yoga classes are available.

West 4 *10A Sutton Lane North, London W4. Tel: 020 8747 1713 www.west4healthclub.co.uk* Staff are helpful here. Nicely equipped.

West London YMCA *14 Bond Street, London W5. Tel: 020 8832 1600 www.westlondonymca.org* Bright and light studios for yoga inside a rather forbidding-looking place. Don't worry – this place is good, so seek and you will find your yoga class and more.

West London Yogashala *Basement, 22 Cleveland Terrace, Bayswater, London W2. Tel: 020 7402 2217 yogashala@btinternet.com www.yogashala.co.uk* Shadow yoga – or as it's often called, Cutting-Edge Hatha yoga – is relatively new to Britain and there are so far only two people qualified to teach it in the country. One of these is William Robertson, who is also a nurse and counsellor. He trained with Shandor Remete in Australia and brought the Shadow style of Hatha yoga to London, setting up a small studio in Bayswater. With roots in Iyengar and Ashtanga Vinyasa yoga, Shadow yoga integrates asanas, breathing and martial arts. This dynamic approach is especially effective in developing resilience, independence, vitality and physical strength. Individual instruction is offered to every student, who is encouraged to practise independently in the warm and welcoming studio. There are also small group classes held on a regular basis for both beginners and the more experienced. Martial Qigong and Qigong for Medical

Therapy are offered in weekly classes as well. Shadow yoga retreats are held in Egypt and Thailand on a regular basis. Nearest tube: Paddington.

Zen Health Centre *32 Notting Hill Gate, London W11. Tel: 020 7229 8666 www.zenhealth.com* Good range of therapies on offer plus yoga classes.

LONDON EAST CENTRAL

Barbican YMCA *Fann Street, London EC2. Tel: 020 7628 0697* In the YMCA tradition: qualified instructors and simple, clean facilities. Let's go!

Champneys Citypoint *1 Ropemaker Street, London EC2. Tel: 020 7920 6200 www.champneyscitypoint.com* Fresh. Sparkling. Never too full. Everything laid on. Careful yoga classes. Indeed, everything you would expect when the price makes it exclusive and is backed by Champneys' long-held and excellent tradition of offering the best of the best. A health juice bar too!

Saddlers Sports & Athletic Club *122 Goswell Road, London EC1. Tel: 020 7505 5656* One of eight public leisure and sports sites of Islington Council, managed professionally. Not many offer yoga but if you have a public centre near you that is not listed here, then check out if they have added yoga to their programme. Saddlers offers yoga along with loads of other activities and exercise equipment.

Vie *122 Clerkenwell Road, London EC1. Tel: 020 7278 8070 www.viehealthclubs.com* Impressive programme of classes and activities but the facility is disappointing for such a prestigious central location. Concentrate on the yoga and never mind the décor.

LONDON EAST

Atherton Leisure Centre *189 Romford Road, London E15. Tel: 020 8536 5500 www.newham.gov.uk*

Bodywise Natural Health Centre *119 Roman Road, London E2. Tel: 020 8458 4716* Associated with the nearby London Buddhist Centre, this alternative health centre is managed by a staff of Buddhist women. Drop-in yoga classes. Calm, peaceful place.

Cathall Millennium Leisure Centre *Cathall Road, London E11. Tel: 020 8539 8343 www.lbwf.gov.uk/leisure* Modern place. Gym. Pool. Wellbeing clinic.

East Ham Leisure Centre *324 Barking Road, London E6. Tel: 0208 548 5850 www.newham.gov.uk* Pools, theatre, dance studio, weights room, steam room plus more. Busy on the weekend and a lot of children. Café. Crèche.

Greens Health & Fitness *Larkswood Leisure Park, 175 New Road, London E4. Tel: 020 8523 7474 www.greensonline.co.uk* Very smart place with high-quality facilities. Lots of classes including yoga.

Holistic Health *64 Broadway Market, London E8. Tel: 020 7275 8434 www.holistic-health-hackney.co.uk*

John Orwell Sports Centre *Tench Street, London E1. Tel: 020 7488 9421 www.towerhamlets.gov.uk* Solid building. Large gym. Massage and yoga included in programme.

Kelscott Leisure Centre *Markhoue Road, London E17. Tel: 020 8520 7464 www.lbwf.gov.uk/leisure* Mirrored studio with over 35 weekly classes including yoga.

London Buddhist Centre *51 Roman Road, London E2. Tel: 0845 458 4718 info@lbc.org.uk www.lbc.org.uk* The Friends of the Western Buddhist Order (FWBO) strive to put Buddhism's essential teachings into practice in the West, and the London Buddhist Centre is part of that worldwide movement. Buddhist classes are offered as well as retreats for people at all levels of experience. There are Gay Men's Retreats, Black People's Retreats, Family Retreats and Parents & Children's Retreats. Open all year Monday–Friday 10am–5pm. Evening and lunchtime classes available. Facilities include library and guest lounge. Nearest tube: Bethnal Green. Buses: 253 and 8.

Peak Fitness *Limeharbour, London E14. Tel: 020 7515 8940 www.peak-fitness.co.uk* Huge complex with tons of stuff on offer.

Queensbridge Sports & Community Centre *30 Holly Street, London E8. Tel: 020 7923 7773* A new sports centre, fully up to date. Good mix of clients. Yoga classes on a regular basis. Café.

Results Health Studio *Hickman Avenue, London E4. Tel: 020 8523 5133 www.resultshealthstudio.co.uk* Personal training, massage, studio for yoga and much more.

Solutions Health & Fitness *135 Wadham Road, London E17. Tel: 020 8531 9358 www.solutionshealthandfitness.com* Busy place but attractive studios and facilities. Lots of classes to choose from.

Spindles *The International Hotel, Marsh Walk, London E14. Tel: 020 7712 0100* A warm welcome from a friendly and informed staff help make this a good place. Yoga and more.

Waltham Forest YMCA *642 Forest Road, London E17. Tel: 020 8509 4600* A relaxed and friendly YMCA with gym and good range of activities.

Wanstead Leisure Centre *Redbridge Lane West, London E11. Tel: 020 8989 1172* Shared with a school so it's busy – and you need to check out hours open to the public. Everything from badminton to yoga on offer.

Whitechapel Sports Centre *Durwood Street, London E1. Tel: 020 7247 7538 www.towerhamlets.gov.uk* Dance and yoga studio, cardio workout, all-weather pitch. Busy, modern place.

Yoga Place E2 *First Floor, 449 Bethnal Green Road, London E2. Tel: 020 7739 5195 www.yogaplace.co.uk* Two studios, more than enough teachers. Some workshops led by well-known teachers. Regular programme.

York Hall Leisure Centre *Old Ford Road, London E2. Tel: 020 8980 2243 www.towerhamlets.gov.uk* Old building but recently refurbished with a new gym. Café.

LONDON SOUTH-EAST

The Active Club at the Holiday Inn *Nelson Dock, 265 Rotherhithe Street, London SE16. Tel: 020 7231 1001* Very popular with locals. Good facilities. Yoga regularly on offer.

Arches Millennium Leisure Centre *80 Trafalgar Road, London SE10. Tel: 020 8317 5000 www.gll.org* Walk through the royal park to find this lovely place. A popular venue and justly so. Busy programme including yoga.

Brockwell Lido *Brockwell Park, London SE24. Tel: 020 8671 4532* Yoga with Nigel Gilderson.

Camberwell Leisure Centre *Artichoke Place, London SE5. Tel: 020 7703 3024 www.fusion-lifestyle.com* Gym club. Pool. Yoga.

The Club at County Hall *County Hall, London SE1. Tel: 020 7928 4900 www.theclubatcountyhall.com* Not too smart but all the stuff you need to work out. Programme includes yoga.

Cold Harbour Millennium Leisure Centre *Chapel Farm Road, London SE9. Tel: 020 8851 8692 www.gll.org* Lottery money built this facility, which has just about everything you could desire in a leisure centre. Staff know what they are doing and the programme includes yoga in excellent studios.

Changing rooms really good. Bar. Crèche.

Colfe's Leisure Centre *Horne Park Lane, Lee, London SE12. Tel: 020 8297 9110* Restricted use sometimes because of local school.

Crystal Palace National Sports Centre *Ledrington Road, London SE19. Tel: 020 8778 0131 www.crystalpalacensc.co.uk* A major athletics stadium and a huge affair – lots of rooms, facilities, pools and even a separate children's gym. Bar. Café. Some facilities are a bit worn out but the yoga classes are very good.

Dulwich Leisure Centre *45 East Dulwich Road, London SE22. Tel: 020 8693 1833 www.southwark.gov.uk* A good place with lots of facilities and equipment. Full programme including yoga.

Elephant & Castle Leisure Centre *22 Elephant & Castle, London SE1. Tel: 020 7582 5505 www.southwark.gov.uk* Fitness and activity classes including yoga.

Flaxman Sports Centre *Carew Street, London SE5. Tel: 020 7926 1054* Friendly place with all the basics.

Kagyu Samye Dzong London *Carlisle Lane, Lambeth, London SE1. Tel: 020 7928 5447 london@samye.org www.samye. org/london* Within walking distance of the Houses of Parliament, Lambeth Palace and Archbishops Park, this centre is an unexpected find in a historic part of London. A former Victorian primary school, the buildings have been converted to provide a large shrine room, library, tearoom and simple dormitory accommodation. Additional premises within the grounds offer space for yoga. There are regular classes in meditation instruction and introductory Buddhism. The centre opened in 1998 and is part of the Samye Ling in Scotland. It is run by Lama Zangmo, a fully ordained nun and the first person in Britain to be given the title of Lama (meaning 'teacher'). In addition to Lama Zangmo, there is a small community of Buddhist monks, nuns and lay people.

Lewis Healthworks *Harris City Technology College, Maberley Road, London SE19. Tel: 020 8461 7510* Open weekends and weekday evenings only. A big facility so lots you could add on to your primary yoga programme.

Miami Health Club *210 Old Kent Road, London SE1. Tel: 020 7703 9811* A recently improved place. Relaxed attitude. Helpful staff. Regular yoga.

Oval Health & Fitness Club *The Oval, London SE11. Tel: 020 7820 5755 www.surreycricket.com* A fitness centre in the Surrey Cricket Club. Regular yoga.

Peckham Pulse *10 Melon Road, Peckham, London SE15. Tel: 020 7525 4999* Fashionably furnished. Pools. Personal fitness programmes.

Physical Arts *10–11 Milroy Walk, Upper Ground, London SE1. Tel: 020 7928 3000 www.physicalarts.com* Refurbished mind and body place.

PhysioActive *Old Bank House, Mottingham Road, London SE9. Tel: 020 8857 6000* Yoga, pilates and other courses on offer at this professionally staffed centre which has as its central aim healing treatment and prevention, particularly related to sports injuries. In the past the yoga class has finished off with a free coffee. Nice.

Plumstead Leisure Centre *Speranza Street, London SE18. Tel: 020 8855 8289* Well equipped with an indoor bowls hall. Regular yoga sessions. Gym. Crèche.

Royal Herbert Leisure Club *Royal Herbert Pavilions, Shooters Hill Road, London SE18. Tel: 020 8319 0720* A small and inviting health club but no real charm to the place. Pool. Bar. It may do for yoga for some, but check out first to see if it's your cup of tea.

Seven Islands Leisure Centre *Lower Road, London SE16.*

Tel: 020 7237 3296 www.springhealthleisure.com A new-look place with good facilities and activities. Café. Kids welcome.

Take Shape *17A Brandram Road, London SE13. Tel: 020 8852 2009* A women-only club. Variety of classes on offer including yoga.

Yoga at Globe House *2A Crucifix Lane, London SE1. Tel: 020 7378 1177 www.lordshiva.net* Peaceful venue. Good staff. No-frills place. Popular.

Wavelength Leisure Centre *Griffin Street, London SE8. Tel: 020 8694 1134 www.lewisham.gov.uk* Impressive building on the edge of the market. Pool. Yoga classes.

Wellingtons Health Club *101 Lower Marsh, London SE1. Tel: 020 7401 8616 www.wellingtonshealthclub.co.uk* Light and spacious health and fitness club. Personal approach.

LONDON SOUTH-WEST

Aquilla Health Club *11 Thurloe Place, London SW7. Tel: 020 7225 0225 www.aquillahealthclub.com* A basement place. Not great for lifting the spirits but scheduled for a full refurbishment so check it out.

Art of Health & Yoga Centre *Tel: 020 8682 1800 www.artofhealth.co.uk* Therapies, exercise classes including yoga, beauty treatments, health and healing sessions.

Balham Leisure Centre *Elmfield Road, London SW17. Tel: 020 8772 9577 www.wandsworth.gov.uk* Recently refurbished to a very high standard, this is an excellent leisure centre with an extensive programme.

Brixton Recreation Centre *27 Brixton Station Road, London SW9. Tel: 020 7926 9780 www.lambeth.gov.uk* Six floors of facilities including yoga classes. Not a place in the best of shape – but all the activities you need to get yourself fit.

The Chelsea Club *Chelsea Village, Fulham Road, London SW6.*

Tel: 020 7915 2200 www.thechelseaclub.com Exclusive. Millions spent on the facility. Bespoke exercise and fitness. Just about as upmarket as you can get. Yoga with all the material life trimmings.

Chelsea Sports Centre *Chelsea Manor Street, London SW3. Tel: 020 7352 6985 www.rbkc.gov.uk* Big but basic building. Alternative therapies available along with regular yoga classes.

Christopher's Squash & Fitness Club *Wimbledon Stadium, Plough Lane, London SW17. Tel: 020 8946 4636* Rough and ready place but yoga held here.

Circle Health Club *The Piper Building, Peterborough Road, London SW6. Tel: 020 7751 0056 www.circlehealthclub.com* A young professionals sort of place with good facilities and a reputation for aspiring to be the best club around. Yoga among other offerings.

Clapham Leisure Centre *141 Clapham Manor Street, London SW4. Tel: 020 7926 0700 www.lambeth.gov.uk* Dance studio, weights room, pools, plus things for kids to do and a programme including yoga.

Club at St James Court *Crowne Place, Buckingham Gate, London SW1. Tel: 020 7963 8307* Fitness, personal training, reflexology, massage, yoga. Smart, clean, relaxed place.

Dolphin Square Sports Club *Dolphin Square, London SW1. Tel: 020 7798 8686 www.dolphinsquarehotel.co.uk* Unwind in this old and famous place, which has a fitness facility in the basement. Walk in, try it out, sign up for yoga.

Earls Court Gym *254 Earls Court Road, London SW5. Tel: 020 7370 1402 www.sohogyms.co.uk* Dance and yoga studio. Fully equipped gym. Not a fussy place. Great atmosphere. Buzzy and busy.

Equis Personal Training *43A Cheval Place, Knightsbridge, London SW7. Tel: 020 7838 1138 www.equis.com* Small yoga classes in this exclusive place where your booking brings lots of personal attention. Pricey.

Family Natural Health Centre *106 Lordship Lane, London SW22. Tel: 020 8693 5515* Great for kids, OK for the family. Nice if you want some noisy joy around you.

The Harbour Club *Watermeadow Lane, London SW6. Tel: 020 7371 7700 www.harbourclub.co.uk* Family orientated. Offers everything you might need from personal training to nutritional advice. Dance, holistic exercise, yoga and much more.

Imperial College Sports Centre *7 Princes Gardens, London SW7. Tel: 020 7594 8964* Popular with college students. Pool. Gym. Yoga. An adequate place but busy and doesn't much inspire.

Karma Limited *263a Fulham Road, Chelsea, London SW3. Tel: 020 7565 5355 yoga@calmerkarma.org.uk www.calmerkarma. org.uk/yoga* Yoga for the London corporate workplace to combat stress. The website title – 'Calmer karma' – says it all. It's a great idea if you can get the boss to agree. Good luck!

Katy Appleton *Open Door Community Centre, Beaumont Road, London SW19. Tel: 020 8788 8892 www.appleyoga.com* A celebrity teacher with regular classes for all, including beginners and open classes. Café.

The Kings Club *Woodhayes Road, Wimbledon, London SW19. Tel: 020 8255 5401 www.kcs.org.uk* Sports centre attached to Kings College School. Not your ideal place but yoga is on offer.

KXGYMUK *151 Draycott Avenue, London SW3. Tel: 020 7584 5333* You pronounce 'kx' as 'kicks'. Big joining fee, but there's everything you could want. In fact, this place seems to have forgotten nothing. A bit overwhelming if all you want is a yoga class. But it might just be the place for you to find your inner peace. Who knows?

Latchmore Leisure Centre *Burns Road, London SW11. Tel: 020 7207 8004 www.wandsworth.gov.uk* Swimming, gym, good changing rooms, exercise studio plus yoga. This place continues its upgrade programme. Check it out.

Lillie Road Fitness Centre *Lillie Road, London SW6. Tel: 020 7381 2183 www.lbhf.gov.uk* The range of gym stuff attracts a lot of male clients. Keen staff. Crèche. Dance studio. Personal training.

London South Bank Club *124–130 Wandsworth Road, London SW8. Tel: 020 7622 6866 www.southbankclub.co.uk* Not much to look at from the outside but inside it's great – trendy surroundings, good facilities, modern gym, regular yoga. Bar.

My Yoga *42 Lavender Hill, London SW11. Tel: 020 7738 1499 www.myyoga.com* One studio with one or two teachers – but do not be put off. There is individual attention, small classes and a peaceful atmosphere. Nice.

Panakeia *44 Pimlico Road, London SW1. Tel: 020 7730 9970 www.panakeia.co.uk* New, friendly place. Loads of different therapies and healing approaches including yoga on offer.

The Peak Health Club *The Carlton Tower London, Cadogan Place, London SW1. Tel: 020 7858 7008 www.carltontower hotel.com* Penthouse yoga classes. Pool.

Queen Mother Sports Centre *223 Vauxhall Bridge Road, London SW1. Tel: 020 7630 5522* A serious gym and fitness place. Sports hall, swimming, good activities programme including yoga.

S. Manoharan Yoga Classes *77 Daybrook Road, London SW19. Tel: 07950 806482 www.omyoga.co.uk* Individual and group classes in Wimbledon and south-west London. Classes for beginners, intermediate and advanced with trained yoga teacher Manoharan.

Sands End Community Centre *59–61 Broughton Road, London SW6. Tel: 020 7736 1724 www.lbhf.gov.uk* A place with a number of different aims from gym to adult learning, but yoga is on offer. The changing facilities and the appearance of the place leave much room for improvement.

Sangam Yoga Centre *80A Battersea Rise, London SW11. Tel: 020 7223 2899 www.sangamyoga.com* Morning and evening classes in a dynamic yoga centre devoted to Ashtanga yoga. Beginners given a warm welcome.

Satyananda Yoga Centre *70 Thurleigh Road, London SW12. Tel: 020 8673 4869*

Sivananda Yoga *Wimbledon, London SW19. Tel: 020 8401 8328* Contact Frances Dunovic – *francisd@ignis.co.uk*

Sivananda Yoga Vendanta Centre *51 Felsham Road, London SW15. Tel: 020 8780 0160 London@sivananda.org www.sivananda.org/london* This place is the spiritual home to people living the yoga lifestyle. All aspects of yoga are featured in a regular programme of activities. There is a free class on Saturday afternoons to learn about yoga. There are yoga vacations, weekend workshops and an open house when demonstrations are given. Children's classes too. Peaceful atmosphere. Café.

Soho Gym *95–87 Clapham High Street, London SW4. Tel: 020 7720 0321 www.sohogyms.co.uk* Dance, exercise, keep fit, yoga, plus more. Lots of music.

South London Natural Health Centre *7A Clapham Common Southside, London SW4. Tel: 020 7720 8817 www.south londonnaturalhealthcentre.com* Body and soul place, lovely atmosphere, good treatments plus yoga on offer.

Streatham Sports Centre *384 Streatham High Road, London SW16. Tel: 020 7926 6744 www.lambeth.gov.uk* Friendly, loud, great little centre, full of energy. Personal instruction available.

Studioflex *26 Priests Bridge, London SW14. Tel: 020 8878 0556* Mind, body and soul centre, rooted in yoga. Smallish classes. Range of yoga forms on offer.

Vitality Centre *Alexander House, 155 Merton Road, London SW18. Tel: 020 8871 4677 www.vitality-centre.co.uk* Recently opened. Offers yoga plus loads of therapies.

YMCA *200 The Broadway, Wimbledon, London SW19. Tel: 020 8542 9055 www.merton.gov.uk* Busy place. Helpful staff. Restaurant. Not an inspiring facility but yoga is on offer and that's what you're going for.

HEALTH CLUB CHAINS

Health club chains like **Esporta, David Lloyd, Cannons, Fitness First, Holmes Place, LA Fitness** and **LivingWell**, all with branches around London, usually offer yoga plus loads of facilities and programmes. You might want to start your enquiry by phoning the general information number or visiting their website.

Cannons *16 clubs in London. Tel: 08707 808 182/020 8336 2288 www.cannons.co.uk*

David Lloyd *7 clubs in London. Tel: 08708 883015 www.davidlloydleisure.co.uk*

Esporta *13 clubs in London. Tel: 08003 776782 www.esporta.com*

Fitness First *27 clubs in London. Tel: 01202 845 222 www.fitnessfirst.com*

Holmes Place *28 clubs in London. Tel: 020 7795 4100 www.holmesplace.com*

LA Fitness *19 clubs in London. Tel: 020 7366 8080 www.lafitness.co.uk*

LivingWell *9 clubs in London. Tel: 01908 308800 www.livingwell.co.uk*

SOUTH-WEST ENGLAND

CORNWALL

BODMIN Lakeview Country Club *Lanivet, Bodmin, Cornwall PL30. Tel: 01208 831808 admin@lakeview-country-club.co.uk www.lakeview-country-club.co.uk/health. html* Country clubs have that *certain something* and Lakeview is no exception. Practise your yoga, then go for a dip in the pool, visit the sauna and steam room, and wrap up and rest in the solarium. Then with a sigh, give yourself over to the experts in the beauty room. Finally, after this exhausting but proper workout and relax programme, you take in the café and bar – maybe even their restaurant if you feel up to a meal. We're on our way back now!

HELSTON Helston Sports Centre *Church Hill, Helston, Cornwall TR13. Tel: 01326 563320* Basic place with yoga once a week plus some other activity classes. Small gym. That's it, folks!

LAUNCESTON Launceston Leisure Centre *Coronation Park, Launceston, Cornwall PL15. Tel: 01566 772551* OK for yoga classes plus fitness classes and a gym for workouts. Café.

PENZANCE John Scott & Lucy Crawford Scott *The Space at Number 8, 8 Chapel Street, Penzance, Cornwall TR18. Tel/Fax: 01736 331972 lucy@ashtanga.co.uk www.ashtanga.co.uk*

PENZANCE Mounts Bay Health Studio *Queens Hotel, The Promenade, Penzance, Cornwall TR18. Tel: 01736 369460* A fully equipped gym here. Yoga and other classes are regularly on offer, including t'ai chi. Go for the carrot and apple in the juice bar – great!

PORTH Trevelgue Hotel *Watergate Road, Porth, Cornwall TR7. Tel: 01637 872864 trevelguehotel@btinternet.com* *www.trevelguehotel.co.uk/health.html* The summertime programme of activities has yoga on offer along with other classes. There's also a pool, gym, sauna, jacuzzi and solarium. Bar.

REDRUTH Carn Brea Leisure Centre *Station Road, Redruth, Cornwall TR15. Tel: 01209 714766* Extensive programme of classes here including yoga for all ages and abilities. There is a 25-metre pool, a gym, sauna and steam room, and a nice sunbed to stretch out on. Then you can laze in the lounge with a coffee from the café. Nice here.

SALTASH Aero Sport, Health & Leisure Club *St Mellion International Hotel, Golf & Country Club, St Mellion, Saltash, Cornwall PL12. Tel: 01579 351351 www.st-mellion.co.uk* Yoga classes plus a gym, pool, sauna, steam room and jacuzzi. Café-bar.

SALTASH China Fleet Country Club *North Pill, Saltash, Cornwall PL12. Tel: 01752 848668 info@china-fleet.co.uk www.china-fleet.co.uk* Love the name of this place – conjures up the misty seas of old Cornwall with sailing ships and smugglers. Regular yoga classes. There is a gym, fitness suite, plunge pool, sauna, steam room and jacuzzi. Complete with bar, restaurant and coffee shop, this has got to be a great place to yoga out.

TRURO Amrit Centre *Truro. Tel: 01726 883811* Contact Shivani

TRURO Ananda Yoga Centre *Truro. Tel: 01872 530317* Contact Nandini Devi

WADEBRIDGE Shipshape Fitness *Roserrow, St Minver, Wadebridge, Cornwall PL27. Tel: 01208 863000* Shipshape Fitness offers yoga, a pool, sauna, steam room, jacuzzi, fitness suite and yoga classes. There is a café-bar – but watch out for the delicious cakes.

DEVON

GENERAL Devon Yoga Teachers' Federation *Tel: 01837 54880* Contact Angela Blezard.

ASHBURTON The Ashburton Centre *79 East Street, Ashburton, Devon TQ13. Tel: 01364 652784 stella@ ashburtoncentre.freeserve.co.uk www.ashburtoncentre.co.uk* The Ashburton Centre for Holistic Education and Training was founded in 1994 to provide personal development, spiritual, healing, environmental and related residential courses within a supportive community. Guests join the community during their stay so that a feeling of belonging and family is generated. Along with yoga, the programme covers a wide variety of activities, such as meditation, Qigong, Shiatsu as spiritual practice, choice and transformation seminars, healing, and voice workshops. The centre is in the town, but there are many good country and woodland walks nearby. Open all year. Accommodation comprises four singles, three twin and two three-bed rooms. No smoking. No outside shoes worn in the house. Facilities include garden, guest lounge, TV. Food is vegetarian. Courses and holidays are also sometimes offered in France and Spain. Access by train: Newton Abbot mainline station is ten minutes away. The centre will collect you. Easy access from M5.

ASHPRINGTON Sharpham College for Buddhist Studies and Contemporary Enquiry *Ashprington, Totnes, Devon TQ9. Tel: 01803 732542 college@sharpham-trust.org* Sharpham College for Buddhist Studies and Contemporary Enquiry occupies a beautiful English Palladian house with views stretching down to the River Dart. It is here that the Sharpham Trust strives to create a new way of education, aiming to achieve a balance between the practical and the spiritual.

Although the approach is Buddhist, it does not adhere to any particular school. The Buddhist studies include Theravada, Indo-Tibetan Mahayana, Zen and Chinese Buddhism, plus Buddhist history, philosophy and psychology, and courses such as the Psychology of Awakening Contemporary Enquiry, Ecology and the Environment, Western Philosophy and Psychology, the New Sciences, and Arts and Culture. The teachers come from a broad spectrum of backgrounds and have long-standing commitments to Buddhism. The college cannot accommodate short-term guests because the programme course students occupy all the living accommodation. Having said that, there is a programme of events that form day educational retreats. Open September to July for students. Closed January and August. Ten single rooms available, garden, library, student lounge, TV. Vegetarian wholefood. See programme brochure for cost of short-term courses.

ASHPRINGTON The Barn *Lower Sharpham Barton, Ashprington, Totnes, Devon TQ9. Tel: 01803 732661 sharpham-barn@dial.pipex.com www.sharpham-trust.org* The underlying purpose of The Barn, which has been going for some thirteen years, is to create a working retreat centre – a place one might visit to retreat temporarily from the world at large, but also to work on the land. The atmosphere is contemplative and there is much silence. During your stay here, you will be expected to be fully involved in the daily schedule of activities and to take your turn preparing vegetarian meals for everyone. One evening a week is devoted to discussing personal matters as well as broader issues that relate to the community's life together. You are encouraged to pursue those activities, such as Buddhist study classes, yoga mornings and listening to cassettes of Dharma talks, which support a contemplative way of life. The daily schedule includes four to five hours' work on the land and three 45-minute periods of group meditation. No previous experience of farm work is necessary. The Barn Community is based on the Buddhist meditation tradition but is non-denominational and does not require people to follow any prescribed methods of practice. Seven single rooms available, garden, library, payphone. Meals are vegetarian. Situated in very quiet countryside – beautiful location on a hillside overlooking the River Dart, with no roads visible. Access by car is best, but enquire if you want to walk from the nearest place served by public transport.

AXMINSTER Axe Valley Sports Centre *Chard Street, Axminster, Devon EX13. Tel: 01297 35235* Yoga. Facilities at Axe Valley include a gym, pool and sunbeds. Good basic centre.

BARNSTAPLE *North Devon Leisure Centre, Seven Brethren Bank, Sticklepath, Barnstaple, Devon EX31. Tel: 01271 373361* Yoga and body balance classes. Facilities include a pool, good gym, sauna, steam room and jacuzzi. Restaurant and bar.

BIDEFORD The Yarner Trust *Welcombe Barton, Welcombe, Bideford, Devon EX39. Tel: 01288 331692 enquiries@ yarnertrust.co.uk www.yarnertrust.co.uk* Getting back to nature is the theme here, with camping in the grounds of Welcombe Barton with coastal and woodland views. Traditional yurts are available for hire and hot showers, barbecue and under-six play areas are provided. A range of creative workshops are available on a daily basis. These range from yoga to rag weaving to wildlife walks. Plenty of other fun things to do in a charming area of Devon.

COMBE MARTIN The Wild Pear Centre *King Street, Combe Martin, Devon EX34. Tel: 0208 883086* The Wild Pear Centre is situated in the North Devon seaside village of Combe Martin, gateway to Exmoor National Park. While there is no garden or grounds at the centre, you can treat the whole area like a wild garden on your doorstep. The centre is available for both residential and non-residential use and hosts different workshops from yoga, meditation, body-work, voicework, movement and dance to personal growth courses. If you are interested in staying here then write in the first instance to Juliana Brown, 36 Womersley Road, Couch End, London N8 9AN (Tel: 020 8341 7226).

CREDITON Lords Meadow Leisure Centre *Commercial Road, Lords Meadow Industrial Estate, Crediton, Devon EX17. Tel: 01363 776190* Go to the yoga class, work out in the gym, take a sauna and swim, have a cool drink. That's it.

CULLOMPTON Culm Valley Sports Centre *Meadow Lane, Cullompton, Devon EX15. Tel: 01884 32853* Yoga, gym, sauna, and a drinks vending machine. Your basic centre and OK.

DARTMOUTH Maitri Centre *Dartmouth, Tel: 01803 833695* Contact Eddie Shapiro. Yoga and other classes on the programme.

EXETER Derek the Dog Studios *3rd Floor, Queens Walk, Exeter EX4. Tel: 01392 255031 info@derekthedog.co.uk*

EXETER Duncan Hulin Holistic Yoga *devonschoolyoga@ eclipse.co.uk* Duncan Hulin holds weekly classes in Exeter and Sidmouth and also foundation and teacher-training courses. He organises yoga holidays in southern Spain and Kerala, South India. There are a number of other yoga sessions and events on offer in his programmes.

EXETER Jenny Kane *Tel: 01884 252940 bearfacelies@ yahoo.com* British Wheel of Yoga diploma teacher with many years of yoga experience and teaching. Her classes are held in Exeter, Cullompton, Uffculme, Crediton and Tiverton.

EXETER Ray Parrott *65 Weavers Court, Commercial Road, Exeter EX2. Tel: 01392 257360 rparrott1@compuserve.co* British Wheel of Yoga teacher with over ten years' teaching experience. He holds regular classes around Exeter. He focuses on Hatha yoga, including meditation, relaxation, breathing and chanting.

EXETER Riverside Leisure Centre *Cowick Street, Exeter, Devon EX4. Tel: 01392 221771 www.ex.ac.uk/brad/noindex/riverside/welcome.htm* Yoga on regular offer. Good health suite here plus gym and pool. Then you can use the sauna, steam room and jacuzzi. Café and bar.

EXETER Sweat & Stretch Fitness Centre *Devon House, Paris Street, Exeter, Devon EX1. Tel: 01392 433656* Yoga, gym, sauna, treatment room. Café and bar.

EXETER Viniyoga Southwest *Exeter. Tel: 01392 438615* Contact Liz Murtha

HONITON Honiton Sports Centre *School Lane, Honiton, Devon EX14. Tel: 01404 42325* A 25-metre pool plus squash court and a good workout gym. No café but drinks vending machine usually operating.

KINGSBRIDGE Quayside Leisure Centre *Rope Walk, Kingsbridge, Devon TQ7. Tel: 01548 857100* Yoga and fitness classes. Good gym and pool plus café and bar. Nice place.

NEWTON ABBOT South Devon Classical Yoga *Newton Abbot. Tel: 01803 812746* Contact Mike Rowe

OTTERY ST MARY Colin Tooze Sports Centre *Cadhay Lane, Ottery St Mary, Devon EX11. Tel: 01404 814317* Here is yoga – four times a week. Gym and lots of other classes. Free coffee after class. Warm welcome in a pleasant place.

PAIGNTON Torbay Leisure Centre *Penwill Way, Paignton, Devon TQ4. Tel: 01803 522240* Offers a six-week yoga course and adds to the pleasure with a gym, pool and squash court.

Then you can go in the sauna, steam room or jacuzzi. Finish off in the café or bar.

PLYMOUTH Derriford Health & Leisure Centre *Derriford Road, Plymouth, Devon PL6. Tel: 01752 792840* This is a basic outfit – yoga classes, gym, sauna. Café and bar. No pool.

PLYMOUTH Fort Stamford Squash & Fitness Centre *Fort Stamford, Plymstock, Plymouth, Devon PL9. Tel: 01752 407999* A pleasant little place with regular yoga classes. Facilities include a small pool, aerobics, sauna, café and bar.

PLYMOUTH Hillcrest Families Centre *Hillcrest Close, Plympton PL7. Tel: 01752 863124 a.cammack@virgin.net* Weekly class, usually on a Tuesday afternoon. Call first and take a yoga mat with you.

PLYMOUTH Satyananda Yoga in Plymouth *56 Salcombe Road, Plymouth PL4. Tel: 01752 660286* Classes with teacher Rishiputra.

PLYMOUTH Triangle Fitness Suite *Cobourg Street, Plymouth, Devon PL1. Tel: 01752 522240* A regular yoga class plus gym, sauna, steam room and sunbed facilities.

SIDMOUTH Devon School of Yoga *Sidmouth. Tel: 01395 512355* Contact Duncan Hulin

SIDMOUTH Sidmouth Sports Centre *Primley, Sidmouth, Devon EX10. Tel: 01395 577679* Loads of classes here including yoga. Basic stuff but all you need for yoga.

TEIGNMOUTH Broadmeadow Sports Centre *Broadmeadow Estate, Teignmouth, Devon TQ14. Tel: 01626 775940* Day and evening yoga classes. Also aerobics and pilates. Two gyms, sports hall, squash court, sauna and sunbed.

TORQUAY The Kevala Centre *Hunsdon Road, Torquay, Devon TQ1. Tel: 01803 215678 info@kevala.co.uk www.kevala.co.uk/yoga/* A modern approach which fits in with the kind of life most of us live today. You can go to weekly and weekend classes but also learn about yoga online. This includes learning about holistic medicine if you want to add on to your understanding of yoga. Bearing in mind that with yoga you are focusing on the mind-body-spirit idea of uniting the whole person, this kind of information could return some quick benefits.

TORQUAY The Rivera Centre Ltd *Chestnut Avenue, Torquay, Devon TQ2. Tel: 01803 299992* A really nice and casual leisure pool with a restaurant and bar for afters. Yoga classes are held on a regular basis and there is a gym, sauna and jacuzzi.

YELVERTON Grimstone Manor *Yelverton, Devon PL20. Tel: 01822 854358 enquiries@grimstonemanor.co.uk www.grimstone.manor.co.uk* Programmes are run throughout the year, but you must join a specific group programme run either by the resident community or visiting groups. Workshops have included Healing Tao Retreat, Vortex Healing, Gestalt Workshop, and Yoga – Sharing the Quest. See website for current programme. There is a brochure available on how to get there, what to take and other basic information.

DORSET

BLANDFORD FORUM Blandford Sports Centre *Milldown Road, Blandford Forum, Dorset DT11. Tel: 01258 455566* General yoga on offer. Two pools and what they call an 'inspired gym'. Squash, badminton, sauna. Tea and coffee available.

BOURNEMOUTH Astanga Yoga *87 Gladstone Road, Bournemouth, Dorset BH7. Tel: 01202 398269 jwebster66@ hotmail.com* Regular Astanga yoga. Contact above number to discuss what is currently available.

BOURNEMOUTH Burlington Sports & Health Club *Owls Road, Bournemouth, Dorset BH5. Tel: 01202 303055* Nice facilities here. Regular yoga class plus gym, pool, sauna, steam room and jacuzzi. Coffee area too.

BOURNEMOUTH David Lloyd Leisure PLC *5 Knole Road, Bournemouth, Dorset BH1. Tel: 01202 394333 www.davidlloydleisure.co.uk* David Lloyd Leisure puts it together for you around the country. Here there is a regular yoga class plus gym, pool, sauna, sunbed, steam room and jacuzzi. Top it off in their rather good restaurant.

BOURNEMOUTH Queens Park Health Club *51 Queens Park South Drive, Bournemouth, Dorset BH8. Tel: 01202 394900* Decent gym and two saunas plus steam and aromatherapy rooms. Yoga is a regular feature in their activities programme. Pool and a bar serving light meals.

BOURNEMOUTH Stokewood Road Fitness Centre *Stokewood Road, Bournemouth, Dorset BH3. Tel: 01202 510436* Yoga, pool, gym and a vending machine for drinks.

BOURNEMOUTH Yoga in Bournemouth *Bournemouth, Dorset BH7. Tel: 07976 626783 jwebster@hotmail.com* Astanga yoga classes. Beginners and advanced students in two different classes. Telephone for details.

BRIDPORT Bridport Leisure Centre *Skilling Hill Road, Bridport, Dorset DT6. Tel: 01308 427389* General yoga class plus pool, gym and massage room. Drinks vending machine.

BROADSTONE Broadstone Leisure Centre *Station Approach, Broadstone, Dorset BH18. Tel: 01202 777766 www.skillsforlife.org* Big pool plus two refurbished gyms. Sauna, steam room, lounge bar and waterside bar. Yoga activities usually on the programme.

CHARMOUTH Monkton Wyld Court *Charmouth, Bridport, Dorset DT6. Tel: 01297 560342 monktonwyldcourt@*

btinternet.com Eleven acres of grounds surround this large Victorian rectory situated in a secluded valley on the Devon–Dorset border where people can hopefully find inner awareness. Monkton is a leading centre for holistic education run by a community with their children and has welcomed many visitors and enjoyed good media coverage of its activities. The emphasis is on encouraging personal and spiritual growth, combined with a firm commitment to ecology, green issues and self-sufficiency (the cows on the farm are hand-milked, for example). There are walks to the sea, peace for meditation and the comforting buzz of a community with a family life. In addition to the yoga courses and retreats, courses in the programmes can be exciting and challenging and offer real potential for self-development and spiritual growth. Some examples include: Non-Violent Communication, Affirming the Female Body, Celebrating Nature, Healing & Evolving Men's Sexuality and Women's Drumming. Weekend retreats include t'ai chi, devotional singing, a work camp, body-mind centring, stained-glass making, drawing, circle and sacred dancing and chanting, shaman dancing and Qigong. Prices are reasonable. Open most of the year. Facilities include garden, library, guest lounge, craft shop, arts and crafts facilities, meditation room, massage and healing room. Children welcomed.

CHRISTCHURCH Two Riversmeet Leisure Centre *Stony Lane South, Christchurch, Dorset BH23. Tel: 01202 477987* Yoga, gym, pool, café and bar.

DORCHESTER Thomas Hardy Leisure Centre *Coburg Road, Dorchester, Dorset DT1. Tel: 01305 266772* Beginners yoga courses and some courses available for intermediate students. A pool and two fitness suites. No café, just a drinks vending machine – but you should always take your water bottle with you anyway.

DORCHESTER Viniyoga South West *Dorchester. Tel: 01305 268639* Contact Domenica Lopane

FERNDOWN Ferndown Leisure Centre *Cherry Grove, Ferndown, Dorset BH22. Tel: 01202 877468* Gym, pool, squash. Yoga classes held on a regular basis. Café. Bar. No sauna.

MUDEFORD Mudeford Community Centre *Pipers Drive, Mudeford, Dorset BH23. Tel: 01590 642882 wendy@uppashaw. powernet.co.uk www.yogaclass.net* Monday yoga class. Mixed ability.

POOLE Anne Vincent Classes *Tel: 01202 676591 anne. vincent@ntlworld.com* British Wheel of Yoga qualified, Anne Vincent teaches in Poole and Talbot Village, Bournemouth. Hatha yoga, gentle yoga, beginners yoga, meditation and chanting, relaxation classes. One-to-one teaching by arrangement.

POOLE Haven Sports & Leisure Club *Banks Road, Poole, Dorset BH13. Tel: 01202 700211* Yoga, gym, indoor and outdoor pools, sauna and steam room. Café. Bar.

POOLE Kemp Welch Leisure Centre *Herbert Avenue, Poole, Dorset BH12. Tel: 01202 738787* Basic place with yoga on offer. Pool and gym. Café.

POOLE Poole Sports Centre *Dolphin Centre, Poole, Dorset BH15. Tel: 01202 777788* 'Skills for life' on offer here – well, at least yoga, a gym, sauna and café. A good start to a new you.

POOLE Yoga with Christopher Gladwell *Poole Yoga Centre, Poole, Dorset BH15. Tel: 01179 244244 www. yogawithchris.co.uk* Monthly class. See website or telephone for current times and dates.

SHERBORNE Gryphon Leisure Centre *Bristol Road, Sherborne, Dorset DT9. Tel: 01935 814011* Go for the yoga class but this is a pretty basic place. Vending machine. Outdoor swimming pool.

VERWOOD Verwood Leisure Centre *Chiltern Drive, Verwood, Dorset BH31. Tel: 01202 826560* General yoga classes on offer plus swimming pool, sports hall and, for afters, a sunbed and bar.

WAREHAM Purbeck Sports Centre *Worgret Road, Wareham, Dorset BH20. Tel: 01929 556454* Regular yoga classes, gym, pool, sauna. Café and bar too.

WEYMOUTH Weymouth Squash & Fitness Centre *Newstead Road, Weymouth, Dorset DT4. Tel: 01305 787000* Sporty place with a gym and health suite. Sauna, steam room and jacuzzi for your wind-down. Bar. Yoga classes usually available throughout the year.

WIMBORNE Gaunts House *Wimborne, Dorset BH21. Tel: 01202 841522 courses@RGF-Gaunt.demon.co.uk* Part of the Gaunts Estate and dedicated to the development of life on a spiritual basis. It offers space and help for spiritual and personal development with a supportive community, all set in beautiful parkland. The facilities are wide-ranging, from a sanctuary to healing rooms. There are many different programmes on offer – during the past year there has been an Easter Yoga Retreat, which included interfaith multicultural programmes, gospel choir, Sanskrit mantra chanting, Native American traditions, Druid traditions and Celtic music. Open all year. Receives men, women, young people, families and groups. Access: train to Poole, bus to Wimborne, then taxi or telephone for a lift.

WIMBORNE Lingfield Health Club *14 Wareham Road, Corfe Mullen, Wimborne, Dorset BH21. Tel: 01202 658188* Check out the yoga class, inspect the gym, swimming pool, sauna and steam room, then have a coffee in the café.

WIMBORNE Queen Elizabeth Leisure Centre *Blandford Road, Hillbutts, Wimborne, Dorset BH21. Tel: 01202 888208*

A good programme of classes including yoga. Gym, pool, steam room and sauna. Bar.

SOMERSET

GENERAL Somerset County Council Adult Learning & Leisure *County Hall, Taunton, Somerset TA1. Tel: 01823 356029 www.learnsomerset.co.uk* Somerset County Council offers an amazing array of yoga classes and courses. In fact, you currently have over 77 classes to choose from. These are spread through the county and are taken by a number of qualified teachers. Enter the above website and search for yoga, select your class, read the details and then send an email to join up. Soon the site will have online enrolment. The yoga classes on offer range from Hatha Yoga, Yoga for all Ages, Astanga Yoga, Dynamic Yoga, Yoga for Wellbeing, Beginners Yoga, Intermediate Yoga, Iyengar Yoga, Yoga for the More Experienced, and Improvers Yoga. The following venues currently offer classes: Bridgwater, Burnham, Castle Carey, Chard, Crewkerne, Dulverton, Frome, Glastonbury, Ilminster, Langport, Shepton Mallet, Stoke sub Hamdon, Taunton and Wellington.

BATH Lansdown Yoga *Bath. Tel: 01225 447498* Contact Janet White

BATH Viniyoga Britain *Bath. Tel: 01225 426327* Contact P. Harvey

BATH Yogaliving *Bath. Tel: 01761 470819* Contact Derek Thorne

BISHOPSTON Yoganjali Yoga Teaching & Therapy Centre *Princes Place, Bishopston, Avon BS7. Tel: 0117 944 2994 info@yoganjali.co.uk www.yoganjali.co.uk* A centre for Viniyoga practice with a wide range of yoga classes, seminars and events. There is even a yoga clinic.

BRISTOL Centre for Yoga Studies *Bristol. Tel: 01179 525612* Contact Marian Miles

BRISTOL Clifton Library *Princess Victoria Street, Clifton, Bristol, Somerset BS8. Tel: 07890 996 782 frankie@dugg. screaning.net* Classes, small group courses and individual sessions are on offer. From time to time an all-day yoga programme is run.

BRISTOL Folk House *40a Park Street, Bristol, Avon BS1. Tel: 0117 926 2987 frankie@dugg.screaning.net* A beginners class. Ring and find out if there is room before going.

BRISTOL Friends Meeting House *127 Hampton Road, Reland, Bristol, Avon BS1. Tel: 07890 996 782 frankie@ dugg.screaning.net* Very popular class so check out if there is room for you. Small groups and individual sessions are on offer by arrangement. Day-long sessions run from time to time.

BRISTOL Relaxation Centre *9 All Saints Road, Clifton, Bristol, Avon BS8. Tel: 07890 996 782* Drop-in class for either the individual session or a course of ten sessions. Small new groups can be started up by arrangement.

BRISTOL Sue Gearing Hatha Yoga *1 Haydens High Street, Wrington, Somerset BS40. Tel: 01934 862279 supeter@ sgearing.freeserve.co.uk* Sue holds classes in Abbots Leigh and also in north Somerset around the Wrington and Burrington area.

BRISTOL Yoga-Vanda Scavelli *Beauley Road, Bristol Southville, Bristol, Avon BS3. Tel: 0117 902 4822 pumulabristol@ yahoo.o.uk* Usually two classes a week, one for beginners.

BRISTOL Yoganjali Yoga Centre *Tel: 01225 426327 paul@viniyoga.co.uk www.viniyoga.co.uk/yoganjali* Viniyoga is on offer here with teacher Paul Harvey, a member of the Viniyoga Britain Association. There are classes during the week suitable for both beginners and intermediates.

MINEHEAD Croydon Hall *Felons Oak, Minehead, Somerset TA24. Tel: 01984 642200 www.croydon.co.uk* Croydon Hall, a large and attractive place, is a recently refurbished mansion near Minehead, surrounded by woodland and views of the Quantock Hills. The nearby Exmoor Park is wonderful for walks, rambling and nature. The house has a comfortable sitting room for guests' use and provides very good vegetarian food. A large number of weekend retreats are held here, run by various expert teachers. Such courses are held in Croydon Hall's leisure suite, which includes a sauna, AromaSpa, hot-tub and mini-gym. There is often massage and reflexology available. Below are two examples of current yoga weekends on offer.

Deep Breath and Yoga for Stress Weekends: These yoga sessions are suitable for all levels, beginners as well as experienced practitioners, with everyone working at their own level. Andrea Fox is an experienced yoga teacher, holding the British Wheel of Yoga Teaching Diploma and the Certificate of Stress Management Training. She also teaches yoga for pregnancy and children's classes.

Astanga Yoga Weekend with Christopher Gladwell: This weekend allows you to explore the Astanga Vinyasa through taught classes and self-practice. Christopher helps you look at techniques for developing awareness of breath, movement and mind, playing with principles of energetics within and out of the yoga practice. You practise deep relaxation and explore how the nature of mind is presented through this. Christopher Gladwell is typical of the qualified teachers that come to Croydon Hall. He has been practising yoga for nearly twenty years after a debilitating back injury led him to it. He qualified as a yoga teacher with the Satyananda School thirteen years ago and has been teaching ever since.

QUEEN CAMEL Self-Realisation Meditation Healing Centre *Laurel Lane, Queen Camel, Near Yeovil, Somerset BA22. Tel: 01935 850266 info@selfrealizationcentres.org www.self realizationcentres.org* A charitable trust run by a team of counsellors and healers living and working together as a family and using the guidance of yoga, meditation and healing self-development in their work and courses. Meditation is a central feature. A seventeenth-century house with extensive grounds of some three and a half acres, the centre offers plenty of space and facilities, including a therapy pool. Near the River Cam and the ancient spiritual centres of Glastonbury and Wells. Visitors have been pleased with the comfort and thoughtfulness of the resident community. Open all year. Facilities include a meditation room, library and guest lounges. Access: car, via A303, or collecting service from the nearest train stations.

TAUNTON Viniyoga Southwest *Taunton. Tel: 01823 322826* Contact Ranju Roy

TAUNTON DEANE Hatha Yoga *Taunton Green. Tel: 01823 667167* Contact Corrine Atherley

WINFORD Winford Manor Retreat *Winford, Bristol, Avon BS18. Tel: 01275 472262* No matter what course or retreat you might choose at Winford Manor, this is without doubt one of the best places. The Manor has gone from strength to strength over the years and guests are welcomed at all times, either to attend courses and retreats or to find space for rest and reflection and to join the community of men and women in the rhythm of a life of prayer. Yoga, of course, but also many other activities such as meditation techniques, reflexology, massage, aromatherapy, assistance in recovery programmes, respite care and counselling, all designed to enhance insight through the study of calligraphy, contemplative dance and Christian and Buddhist spirituality. Creativity is encouraged. Open all year. There is a garden, park, excellent library, and a spacious, comfortable guest lounge. Children welcomed. Access: train: Bristol Temple Meads station seven miles away. Bus: Central Bristol bus station. Car: via A38 from Bristol to Exeter Road.

WILTSHIRE

CALNE White Horse Leisure Centre *Silver Street, Calne, Wiltshire SN11. Tel: 01249 814032* A general yoga course, suitable for most ages and abilities. There is a gym, pool, sauna, steam room and sunbed, plus a café.

CHIPPENHAM Olympiad Leisure Centre *Monkton Park, Chippenham, Wiltshire SN15. Tel: 01249 444144* Olympiad offers a general yoga course. Facilities include a good gym, squash courts, and sauna and steam room plus jacuzzi. Café and bar.

CHIPPENHAM Sheldon Sports Hall *Hardenhuish Lane, Chippenham, Wiltshire SN14. Tel: 01249 651056* Big sports hall with a dance studio. Yoga regularly on offer. A small café completes the picture.

DEVIZES Devizes Leisure Centre *Southbroom Road, Devizes, Wiltshire SN10. Tel: 01380 728894* Nice outfit – a pool, gym, exercise classes and a general yoga class suitable for all. Café.

MARLBOROUGH Marlborough Youth Centre *St Margaret's Mead, Marlborough, Wiltshire SN8. Tel: 01672 512 762*

MARLBOROUGH The European Shiatsu School *High Banks, Lockeridge, Nr Marlborough, Wiltshire SN8. Tel: 01672 513444* Contact Chris Jarmey. Now what, you might ask, is shiatsu doing in this book? Simply because it is the European

School and when you have advanced a bit with your yoga you may well want to take a little look at the ancient liberation and healing art of shiatsu. So why not start here if you live anywhere near Marlborough?

MELKSHAM Christie Miller Sports Centre *32 Lancaster Road, Bowerhill, Melksham, Wiltshire SN12. Tel: 01225 702826* Good facilities to go with your yoga class here. Sports hall, bowling, gym, bar and restaurant. Chill out!

RUSHALL Mysore-Style Yoga *Rushall Village, Village Hall, Rushall, Wiltshire SN9.* Once-a-month Mysore-style yoga with Christopher Gladwell (see Somerset). Contact Emma Pettitt on 01980 670 510.

SALISBURY Downton Leisure Centre *Wick Lane, Downton, Salisbury, Wiltshire SP5. Tel: 01725 513668* With two indoor tennis courts, a gym and regular yoga classes, this is your 'let's just get down to it' facility. Sunbed. Refreshments available at reception.

SWINDON Club 2000 *Hobley Road, Swindon, Wiltshire SN3. Tel: 01793 828124* Gym, pool, sauna, steam room, jacuzzi and loads of classes on the programme. In addition to general yoga, there's Power yoga and a mix of yoga and aerobics classes – sounds like fun. Small café.

SWINDON Fitness 2000 *Hobley Drive, Lower Stratton, Swindon, Wiltshire SN3. Tel: 01793 333666 jane@lanefamily. freeserve.co.uk* Mixed-ability class offered each week, suitable for beginners. Drop-in class so phone to reserve your place.

SWINDON Lime Kiln Leisure Centre *Lime Kiln, Wootton Bassett, Swindon, Wiltshire SN4. Tel: 01793 852197* Two yoga classes, one for beginners and one for intermediates. Tennis courts, a gym, squash courts and a sports hall. Bar too.

SWINDON Oasis Leisure Centre *North Star Avenue, Swindon, Wiltshire SN2. Tel: 01793 445401* Body balance yoga and pilates classes. An interesting lagoon-shaped pool with slides and a wave machine. Gym. Wholefood café.

SWINDON Railway Village Fitness Centre *Unit 3–5 Station Industrial Estate, London Street, Swindon, Wiltshire SN1. Tel: 01793 497123* Women-only gym as well as a mixed gym. Many classes on offer in the programme.

SWINDON Ridgeway Leisure Centre *Inverary Road, Wroughton, Swindon, Wiltshire SN4. Tel: 01793 813280* Fitness is the key here with a 25-metre swimming pool, a good fitness suite, sauna and yoga courses. Drinks vending machine.

SWINDON Swindon & District Yoga Association *Swindon. Tel: 01793 721230* Contact Connie Pearce

TROWBRIDGE Castle Place Leisure Centre *Level 5a Multi-Storey Park, Castle Street, Trowbridge, Wiltshire BA14. Tel: 01225 762711* General yoga on offer along with a grand gym, squash courts, dance studio, lounge area and coffee bar. Go for it!

WARMINSTER Warminster Sports Centre *Woodcock Road, Warminster, Wiltshire BA12. Tel: 01985 212946* Beginners yoga courses – in fact, there can be up to four a week. Intermediate classes too. Gym and pool plus sunbed.

WESTBURY Astanga Yoga *Westbury. Tel: 01373 859313* Contact Allan Oakman

SOUTH AND SOUTH-WEST

BERKSHIRE

GENERAL Yoga Teachers' Circle *Tel: 0118 989 3345.* Contact Raye Lomax

BRACKNELL Bracknell Sport & Leisure Centre *South Hill Road, Bracknell, Berkshire RG12. Tel: 01344 454203* Gym, swimming pool, aerobics, table tennis, squash, sunbeds, jacuzzi. Yoga courses on a regular basis and you pay per session. A friendly place.

COOKHAM Pinder Hall *Cookham, Berkshire SL6. Tel: 01628 770796 rawlinson@waitrose.com* Weekly and drop-in Iyengar-style yoga classes with qualified teacher Margaret Rawlinson.

CROWTHORNE Morgan Centre *Wellington Road, Crowthorne, Berkshire RG11. Tel: 01344 645441 yogasana64@ hotmail.com*

HUNGERFORD Hungerford Leisure Centre *Priory Road, Hungerford, Berkshire RG17. Tel: 01488 683303* Turn-up yoga session. Swimming pool, sunbeds, badminton and two outdoor tennis courts.

MAIDENHEAD Body Zone *The Magnet Leisure Centre, Holmanleaze, Maidenhead, Berkshire SL6. Tel: 01628 639955* Beginners and intermediate yoga classes. Facilities include gym, pool, squash, badminton, outdoor tennis courts. Crèche. Café.

MAIDENHEAD Claires Court School *Maidenhead, Berkshire SL6. Tel: 01628 770796 rawlinson@waitrose.com* Iyengar-style yoga classes with qualified teacher Margaret Rawlinson.

MAIDENHEAD Meridian Health & Fitness Club *Crown Lane, Maidenhead, Berkshire SL6. Tel: 01628 544044* Beginners yoga, general yoga three times a week and Power yoga. There are two studios plus gym, pool, sauna and sunbeds. Café.

NEWBURY Cannons Health Club *The Racecourse, Newbury, Berkshire RG14. Tel: 01635 569966* Regular yoga classes plus pilates. Facilities are good, including pool, gym, full studio, squash, badminton, beauty salon, spa, steam room and jacuzzi. Café and restaurant. We liked it.

NEWBURY Greenacre Leisure Centre *Greenham Road, Newbury, Berkshire RG14. Tel: 01635 41707* This centre is rather divided between what you can use as a member and what you can do if you are not. Members only can use the pool, for example. Facilities open to all are the yoga classes, gym, tennis, squash, badminton, café and bar.

NEWBURY LivingWell Health Club *Oxford Road, Newbury, Berkshire RG14. Tel: 01635 247020 www.livingwell.co.uk* Setting up to offer yoga, so check it out. Pilates class is running at the moment.

NEWBURY Northcroft Leisure Centre *Northcroft Lane, Newbury, Berkshire RG14. Tel: 01635 31199* The class on offer is not general yoga but a body balance course mixing yoga, pilates and t'ai chi. We have some reservations about this kind of mix, because unless it is a specifically developed body balance system, then the teacher really needs training in all three disciplines. Go and talk about it with them and watch one of the classes. If it looks good, it probably is good. Pool, gym, squash, badminton and basketball, crèche, café and bar.

NEWBURY Woodbridge Room *Cromwell Place, Newbury, Berkshire RG14. Tel: 07944 196088 martinyoga@martinyoga. freeserve.co.uk*

READING Andrew Pooley Yoga *Reading, Berkshire. Tel: 0118 978 9112 www.yogaheart.co.uk* Andrew Pooley holds classes in Wokingham and Reading and offers one-to-one teaching in various styles of yoga. He has a fairly active programme so it is well worth finding out what he may be offering near your home or office.

READING Cotswold Sports Centre *Downs Way, Tilehurst, Reading, Berkshire RG31. Tel: 0118 941 4690* Yoga courses which last six weeks and just-turn-up yoga sessions. Basic facilities with a gym, badminton, basketball, outdoor tennis courts and a crèche. Good atmosphere and helpful staff.

READING David Lloyd Club *Thames Valley Park Drive, Reading, Berkshire RG6. Tel: 0118 966 2904 www.davidlloyd leisure.co.uk* David Lloyd clubs are for members only but they set a quality standard in almost every branch of their leisure business. Most of the basic facilities plus regular yoga on offer.

READING Drake Centre *Pangbourne College, Pangbourne, Reading, Berkshire RG8. Tel: 0118 984 4988* Pop-in yoga sessions which are great – except we think a regular weekly group gives that additional pull to get to the class. This is a facility that is shared with a school so it will be busy. Badminton, squash and fitness suite.

READING Earley Community Resource Centre *Warbler Drive, Earley, Reading, Berkshire RG6. Tel: 0118 987 2368 margaret.manning@btinternet.com*

READING Fitness Factory *Rivermead Leisure Complex, Richfield Avenue, Reading, Berkshire RG1. Tel: 0118 901 5000 info@readingleisure.co.uk www.readingleisure.co.uk* Fitness Factory have three sites in Reading – this one, the Arthur Hill Pool & Fitness Studio and the Palmer Park Sports Stadium (although only Rivermead offers yoga at present). If you become a member you get a passport to all three sites. The facilities are fairly standard and include everything you will need for a fitness regime – gym, pool and relaxation kit. Take a look at their website to get a feel for what is on offer.

READING Loddon Valley Leisure Centre *Chalfont Way, Earley, Reading, Berkshire RG6. Tel: 0118 931 2066* Mixed-ability yoga class. Good facilities with a gym, pool, badminton, squash, tennis, basketball, netball, sunbeds and a crèche. Café.

READING Quaker Meeting House Yoga Classes *Church Street, Reading, Berkshire RG1. Tel: 0118 926 4378 chris@ life-times.demon.co.uk bruce.singleton@virgin.net www.life-times.co.uk*

READING Woodford Park Leisure Centre *Haddon Drive, Woodley, Reading, Berkshire RG5. Tel: 0118 969 0356* Two yoga courses on offer as well as pilates, body balancing and other classes. Badminton, short tennis, crazy golf... and then you hit the bar. Good times!

READING Yoga with Kim Allyson *The Triangle, School Road, Tilehurst, Berkshire RG31. Tel: 0118 961 4627 kim.allyson@ ntlworld.com www.yoga-reflexology.co.uk* Kim Allyson teaches a great many popular yoga classes in Berkshire. You should call her to discuss venues and courses or you can email her for an enrolment form. She also runs Yoga Detox Days over a weekend, which consist of yoga, relaxation and meditation, with raw energy foods and herbal detox. Sounds great!

READING Yoga with Veronika *Tel: 0208 352 2657/07799 532826 veronikapenadere@hotmail.com* Veronika Pena de la Jara teaches Hatha yoga and traditional classes in London and Reading. She takes a lot of classes and is well known in local yoga circles. Contact her for details and discuss what would suit you.

SLOUGH Dragons Health Centre *Buckingham Avenue, Slough Trading Estate, Slough, Berkshire SL1. Tel: 01753 553888 www.dragons.co.uk* A members-only place but loads of facilities on offer. Yoga classes during the week including Power and Hatha yoga. Pool and gym.

SLOUGH Langley Leisure Centre *Parlaunt Road, Slough, Berkshire SL3. Tel: 01753 544141* Two types of classes here, one general yoga and the other yoga plus pilates. Pool, gym, aerobics, spa and steam room. Other classes on offer include aerobics and a trim-the-tum-and-bum course. This is a small-ish complex with a pleasant, friendly atmosphere.

SLOUGH Pinnacle Health & Leisure Club *Wexham Street, Stoke Poges, Slough, Berkshire SL3. Tel: 01753 663666* Six classes of yoga for beginners to experienced students. Facilities include a pool, spa, jacuzzi, sauna, steam room, crèche and bar.

WINDSOR Living Yoga *Clewer St Stephen's Church Hall, Vansittart Road, Windsor, Berkshire SL1. Tel: 020 8898 0978 tuesday@yoga.greatxscape.net tuesdaymcneill@yahoo.co.uk* Weekly class of Sivananda yoga with British Wheel of Yoga teacher Tuesday McNeill.

WINDSOR Windsor Leisure Centre *Stovell Road, Windsor, Berkshire SL4. Tel: 01753 850004* Loads of classes here at the Windsor. Mixed-ability classes plus antenatal yoga. Two pools, a gym and a sports hall with racquet sports plus crèche and café. Get here and get started!

WOKINGHAM Nirvana Spa *Mole Road, Wokingham, Berkshire RG41. Tel: 0118 977 1777 www.nirvana-spa.co.uk* Regular classes in yoga, no less than seven different pools (do they really need that many?), two gyms, sauna and steam room, jacuzzi and a crèche. Café, bar and restaurant. With all that swimming, we fell happy and exhausted into the café.

WOKINGHAM Pinewood Hall *Pinewood Leisure Centre, Old Wokingham Road, Wokingham, Berkshire RG40. Tel: 0118 989 1838 liz.osman@ntlworld.com*

WOKINGHAM Pulse 8 Health and Fitness Club *Mole*

Road, Sindlesham, Wokingham, Berkshire RG41. Tel: 0118 977 4729 www.pulse8healthclub.com Members only. Yoga classes. The centre puts the emphasis on fitness. Crèche. Café.

WOKINGHAM Rose Street Methodist Church Hall *Wokingham, Berkshire RG40. Tel: 0118 973 7053 dimead@ hotmail.com tradyoga@hotmail.com*

WOKINGHAM St Sebastian Memorial Hall *Nine Mile Ride, Wokingham, Berkshire RG40. Tel: 01344 645441 yogasna64@hotmail.com*

WOKINGHAM Winnersh Community Centre *New Road, Sindlesham, Wokingham, Berkshire RG41. Tel: 0118 934 9143 meek_karen@hotmail.com*

WOKINGHAM Woosehill Community Centre *Wokingham, Berkshire RG40. Tel: 0118 978 9112 lotus@hotmail.com* Weekly Ashtanga yoga classes with registered Sivananda teacher Andrew Pooley.

HAMPSHIRE

ALRESFORD Perin's Health & Fitness Suite *Pound Hill, Alresford, Hampshire SO24. Tel: 01962 735819* Neat place with a warm welcome, which yet again proves small is beautiful. Yoga class, usually Hatha style, gym, aerobics, tone-up sessions and circuit training. Juice bar.

ALTON Satchidananda Wholistic Trust *Tel: 01420 561054* Contact Swami Satchidananda Ma

ANDOVER Peak Health & Fitness Club *Greycroft House, North Way, Andover, Hampshire SP10. Tel: 01264 392239* Weekly yoga class, which is a real mix of a number of systems and approaches. It includes bits of Hatha, Raja, Ashtanga and Vinyasa systems. We do confess to getting a little uneasy when too many different approaches are combined in what, after all, is a short period like an hour's class, but yoga is a developing art in the West, so we have to expect to come across teaching like that.

ANDOVER Red Rice Health & Fitness *Red Rice, Andover, Hampshire SP11. Tel: 01264 710555 health-fitness@redrice. co.uk* Pool on its way. Meanwhile there are yoga classes, gym, spinning and bikes, steam room and a jacuzzi. Crèche for the kids.

BASINGSTOKE Basingstoke Sports Centre *Porchester Square, Basingstoke, Hampshire RG21. Tel: 01256 326331 www.bassports.co.uk* Loads of classes here including yoga and pilates. A popular and friendly place with a gym, weights room, badminton, squash, sauna and steam room, plus a 25-metre swimming pool. Bar serves meals too.

BASINGSTOKE Kempshott Village Hall *Stratton Park, Off Pack Lane. Basingstoke. Hampshire RG22. Tel: 01256 412665*

BASINGSTOKE Sukha Yoga Club *Tel: 01256 762417* Contact Jill Cossins

BROCKENHURST The Carat Club *Careys Manor Hotel, Lyndhurst Road, Brockenhurst, Hampshire SO42. Tel: 01590 623551 careysmanorhotel@btinternet.com* A pleasant place to go for your yoga class, where you will also find swimming, gym, sauna, steam room, jacuzzi, a range of therapies and a nice restaurant.

EASTLEIGH Fleming Park Leisure Centre *Fleming Park, Passfield Avenue, Eastleigh, Hampshire SO50. Tel: 02380 684800 www.dcleisure.co.uk* A good facility with regular yoga classes, a swimming pool, gym, aerobics, squash, tennis, badminton, steam and jacuzzi plus bar and café.

EMSWORTH Sue Treagust Yoga *11 Beach Road, Emsworth, Hampshire PO10. Tel: 01243 376142 www.kevala.co.uk* Iyengar yoga classes. See the website for details of Sue's classes.

FAREHAM Castle Street Centre *Castle Street,*

Portchester, Fareham, Hampshire PO16. Tel: 02392 640522 KinThayanukulvat@aol.com Mixed-ability classes, suitable for all.

FAREHAM Crofton Community Centre *Stubbington Lane, Stubbington, Fareham, Hampshire PO14. Tel: 02392 640522 KinThayanukulvat@aol.com* Mixed-ability classes, suitable for all.

FAREHAM Fareham Leisure Centre *Park Lane, Fareham, Hampshire PO16. Tel: 01329 233652* Classes for beginners and experienced yoga students. Gym, two pools, café and restaurant. A place to relax and get fit with an easy-does-it attitude.

FAREHAM Neville Lovett Community School *St Anne's Grove, Fareham, Hampshire PO14. Tel: 01329 281808 harvey8@supanet.com*

FARNBOROUGH Farnborough Recreation Centre *Westmead, Farnborough, Hampshire GU14. Tel: 01252 370411* Yoga classes for beginners and intermediates. No need to book. Swimming, aerobics, sauna and sunbeds. Refurbishment, including a bar, is under way.

FARNBOROUGH Holy Trinity Church Hall *Hawley Road, Blackwater, Hampshire GU17. Tel: 01276 609743 judya@talk21.com.uk* Mixed-ability classes also suitable for beginners. Held several times each week.

FLEET Hart Leisure Centre *Hitches Lane, Fleet, Hampshire GU13. Tel: 01252 629974* A class which combines yoga and pilates plus facilities like a pool, gym, aerobics class, tennis, badminton, squash and sunbeds. Café.

HOOK Sacred Heart Catholic Church *London Road, Hook, Hampshire RG27. Tel: 01256 761353 itswellsy@hotmail.com/yoga www.w3b-ink.co/yoga*

LIPHOOK Champneys Forest Mere Health Farm

Liphook, Hampshire GU30. Tel: 01428 727722 enquiries@ henlowgrange.co.uk www.healthfarms.co.uk A top end of the market club and fitness centre. Club members only but there are plenty of facilities to enjoy from yoga classes, pool, steam room and jacuzzi to fitness studios, massages and beauty treatments. Book in for a short stay. Retreat from the world now.

LYMINGTON Everton Pavilion *Frys Lane, Everton, Lymington, Hampshire SO41. Tel: 01590 644551*

LYMINGTON Lymington Recreation Centre *North Street, Lymington, Hampshire SO41. Tel: 01590 670333* Great fitness suite and a 25-metre swimming pool. Turn-up yoga sessions, usually Hatha yoga system. Beginners and improvers both welcomed.

NETLEY MARSH Netley Marsh Community Hall *Woodlands Road, Netley Marsh, Hampshire SO40. Tel: 023 80874874 Lifelonglearning@totton.ac.uk* (mark emails for the attention of the yoga tutor for adult education).

NEW MILTON Ashley Junior School *Ashley Road, New Milton, Hampshire BH25. Tel: 01590 642882 wendy@ uppashaw.powernet.co.uk www.yogaclass.net* Mixed-ability classes.

NEW MILTON New Milton Recreation Centre *Gore Road, New Milton, Hampshire BH25. Tel: 01425 617441* Seven-week yoga course. Swimming pool, gym, sports injury massage sessions if you need them, aromatherapy for relax-ation, and sauna. A place to chill out.

PORTCHESTER Portchester Community School *Portchester, Fareham, Hampshire PO16. Tel: 02392 364399*

PORTSMOUTH The Arts Centre *Reginald Road, Southsea, Portsmouth, Hampshire PO4. Tel: 02392 833025* Mixed-ability class. Bring your own mat and a blanket for relaxing on.

PORTSMOUTH Friendship House *Elmgrove Road, Southsea, Portsmouth, Hampshire PO5. Tel: 02392 361057*

PORTSMOUTH Roko Health & Fitness Club *442 Copnor Road, Portsmouth, Hampshire PO3. Tel: 02392 651400 info@roko@ibltd.com www.health-club.roko.co.uk/portsmouth* Astanga yoga classes, pilates classes, pool, body-building, spa, tennis, squash and jacuzzi. Bar and restaurant.

PORTSMOUTH Southsea Community Centre *St Paul's Square, King Street, Southsea, Portsmouth, Hampshire PO5. Tel: 02392 361057*

PORTSMOUTH Southsea Infants School *Collingwood Road, Southsea, Portsmouth, Hampshire PO5. Tel: 02392 640522*

PORTSMOUTH Trinity Methodist Church *Albert Road, Southsea, Portsmouth, Hampshire PO4. Tel: 02392 361057 ishbel.marquis@breathemail.net*

REDBRIDGE Redbridge School *Cuckmere Lane, Redbridge, Hampshire SO16. Tel: 02380 786485*

RINGWOOD David Lloyd Leisure PLC *242 Christchurch Road, Ringwood, Hampshire BH24. Tel: 01425 470101 www.davidlloydleisure.co.uk* Yoga classes for beginners, intermediates and advanced. The facility is up to the usual David Lloyd Leisure Group standard. Members only, of course.

SHIRLEY Yoga School *28 Arthur Road, Shirley, Hampshire SO15. Tel: 02380 632881* Classes by appointment only.

SOUTHAMPTON Bitterne Leisure Centre *Dean Road, Southampton, Hampshire SO18. Tel: 02380 437647* Pool, fitness suite, aerobics, yoga classes.

SOUTHAMPTON David Lloyd Leisure Centre *Frogmore Lane, Southampton, Hampshire SO16. Tel: 01962 864823 www.litlegemsyoga.co.uk* Well equipped for fitness, relaxing and fun. Yoga classes for pregnant women. Please check out your teacher's qualifications, visit a class and talk to the other mothers-to-be.

SOUTHAMPTON Hampshire Tennis & Health Club *Botley Road, West End, Southampton, Hampshire SO30. Tel: 02380 361122* Inside and outdoor pools, fitness suite, sauna, steam room, jacuzzi and crèche. The yoga classes are a mixture of t'ai chi, Hatha yoga and Power Chi, with some emphasis on body balance. Restaurant. We liked this place a lot.

SOUTHAMPTON Karuna Yoga School *79 Clarendon Road, Southampton SO16. Tel: 01703 632881* Contact Fiona Ashdown

SOUTHAMPTON Noadswood School *North Road, Dibden Purlieu, Southampton, Hampshire SO45. Tel: 02380 874874 (Totton College)* These classes need to be booked through Totton College.

SOUTHAMPTON Southampton Yoga Association *60 Radway Rd, Shirley, Southampton SO1. Tel: 01727 857224* Contact Dr A.K. Shahani

WICKHAM Park Place Pastoral Centre *Winchester Road, Wickham, Fareham, Hants PO17. Tel: 01329 833043 park-placec@aol.com* Lots of room here, including a self-catering wing. Situated in some eighteen acres of grounds, overlooking open countryside. The centre is fairly booked up by parish church groups because they are geared to group bookings – but it's a good place for a family to go on retreat. Open all year except August. Conferences, garden, book shop. Everyone eats together. Traditional food. Vegetarians catered for. Access: see brochure.

WINCHESTER Well House Holistic Health Centre *13 St Thomas Street, Winchester, Hampshire SO23. Tel: 01420 549886 melanie.pickard@virgin.net* General yoga class where the teaching focuses on body, breath and mind.

WINCHFIELD Winchfield Village Hall *Station Road, Winchfield, Hartley Wintney, Hook, Hampshire RG27. Tel: 01256 882573 judith.hayes@tesco.net www.w3b-ink.com/yoga* Yoga classes almost every day during the week.

YATELEY Frogmore Leisure Centre *Frogmore Community Centre, Potley Hill Road, Yateley, Hampshire GU46. Tel: 01252 873454* A community centre with a lot going for it. There are yoga classes for both beginners and intermediates along with a gym, aerobics, sauna and steam room, sunbeds and most racquet sports including squash and badminton. No café but who cares?

YATELEY The Tythings *Reading Road, Yateley, Hampshire GU46. Tel: 0118 9737053 dimead@hotmail.com* Mixed-ability yoga classes. Relaxation included.

Kent

ASHFORD Contours Fitness Studio *Stour Leisure Centre, Tannery Lane, Ashford, Kent TN23. Tel: 01233 664660* Lots going on here. Yoga, body balance, aerobics, t'ai chi, pilates, plus gym, pool, health suite with sauna, sunbeds and massage. Beginners are welcomed here. Body and fitness workouts include trimming up the tums and bums. Café and bar.

ASHFORD Metropolitan Club *Simone Weil Avenue, Ashford, Kent TN24. Tel: 01233 624439* Hatha yoga class. Other classes include body pumping, step work, stability ball and circuit training.

ASHFORD Stour Centre *Tannery Lane, Ashford, Kent TN23. Tel: 01233 639966* Beginners yoga class held several times a week. Facilities include a pool, gym, sauna and steam room, and a health and beauty suite. Fairly basic but OK.

AYLESFORD The Friars *Aylesford Priory, Aylesford, Kent ME20. Tel: 01622 717272 friarsprior@hotmail.com* The

Carmelite Friars say that hope is a source of joy and that joy is a source of strength. At Aylesford they offer an open door to everyone seeking spiritual renewal. The Marian Shrine is a special feature. The retreat programme is a solid one. Here are some examples you might find on offer: inner child retreat, a singles weekend for those who live their baptismal calling as a single person, looking at different Carmelite themes for modern people, Holy Week and Lenten retreats, and an introduction to the spirituality of St John of the Cross. There are yoga and pilates weekends with qualified and experienced teachers and speakers. To find out more about these, contact Inner Light Yoga & Health Company at rms@globalnet.co.uk. Open all year. Disabled access. Conferences, guest lounge, payphone. Children welcome. Guests eat together. Traditional food. Vegetarian and special diets catered for. Access: map and directions in brochure.

AYLESFORD Larkfield Leisure Centre *New Hythe Lane, Larkfield, Aylesford, Kent ME20. Tel: 01622 719345* Lifestyle yoga, which means a combination of systems and movements. Pool, gym, fitness consultants, lots of classes including aerobics and circuit training, sauna and steam room. Children welcomed.

BECKENHAM Amida Racquets & Fitness Spa *Stanhope Grove, Beckenham, Kent BR3. Tel: 020 8658 2200* Big. New. Modern. 100,000 square feet of facilities at your disposal. Athletes, executives, families, the glamorous and successful all come here.

BECKENHAM Langley Park Girls' School Sports Centre *South Eden Park Road, Beckenham, Kent BR3. Tel: 020 8663 1906* Get to the school and you will find a path that leads to this OK but simple place. This is not glamour gym or yoga heaven, but it works.

BECKENHAM The Public Hall *Bromley Road, Beckenham, Kent BR3. Tel: 020 8467 9930 sherig@btinternet.com www. yogaworkswithsheri.co.uk*

BECKENHAM The Spa at Beckenham *24 Beckenham Road, Beckenham, Kent BR3. Tel: 020 8650 0233* Impressive range of facilities in a modern centre. Two pools to dip into after yoga. Popular and friendly.

BEXLEY St James the Great Church Hall *37 Bladindon Drive, Bexley, Kent DA5. Tel: 020 8303 7315* Hatha yoga, which includes breathing exercises, stretching and relaxation.

BEXLEYHEATH Broadways Health Club *2a Devonshire Road, Bexleyheath, Kent DA6. Tel: 020 8304 4919* Relaxation and yoga courses plus gym, aerobics, pilates and boxing.

BEXLEYHEATH Crook Log Sports Centre & Olympia Fitness Studio *Crook Log, Brampton Road, Bexleyheath, Kent DA7. Tel: 020 8304 5386/020 8306 0022 www.leisurelink. uk.com* Good standard of facilities. A lot to enjoy including a bar with food.

BIGGIN HILL Darwin Leisure Centre *Jail Lane, Biggin Hill, Kent TN16. Tel: 01959 540606* This place isn't hidden, but it's not an easy sort of find. A dual-purpose place with a school. Check out how long you are required to join for and be sure it's right for you.

BROMLEY Classic Gym Company *31–33 East Street, Bromley, Kent BR1. Tel: 020 8460 3725* No frills – yoga classes, aerobics, spin class, personal training, gym and sauna. Just what the doctor ordered.

BROMLEY LA Fitness *31–33 East Street, Bromley, Kent BR1. Tel: 020 8460 3725 www.lafitness.co.uk* Yoga and pilates. Over-the-top sales pitch to become a member. We weren't keen.

BROMLEY NJL Fitness Academy *415–421 Bromley Road, Bromley, Kent BR1. Tel: 020 8698 1007* New club, good facilities, relaxation room, regular offering of yoga classes.

BROMLEY The Pavilion Leisure Centre *Kentish Way, Bromley, Kent BR1. Tel: 020 8313 9911* On top of a car park with lots of carpeting and loads of kids. Café and snacks. Pool.

CANTERBURY Centre Space *3 Alcroft Grange, Tyler Hill, Canterbury CT2. Tel: 01227 462038* Yoga, meditation, music, painting, calligraphy, healing therapies, inner growth courses, sacred dancing and day conferences, as well as the private personal retreat. There is a quiet room, woodland and that special place – a Hermit Hut. Open all year. Facilities include garden, library and guest lounge.

CANTERBURY Energy Fitness Ltd *Invicta House, 19–23 Lower Bridge Street, Canterbury, Kent CT1. Tel: 01227 463737* Yoga class taught by Hayley Warren.

CANTERBURY Jackey Thurston Yoga *Canterbury, Kent CT1. Tel: 01303 893911* British Wheel of Yoga foundation in yoga course. Jackey Thurston also teaches in Whitstable.

CANTERBURY Kingsmead Leisure Centre *Kingsmead Road, Canterbury, Kent CT2. Tel: 01227 769818* Popular place and can get very busy. Limited space in classes so book early. Pools, gym, aerobics. Cake and coffee served.

CHATHAM Lordswood Leisure Centre *North Dane Way, Chatham, Kent ME5. Tel: 01634 682862* Basic place – yoga, health suite, aerobics and beauty treatments.

CHISLEHURST Eden *Sidcup Bypass, Chislehurst, Kent BR7. Tel: 020 8308 3900* Upmarket. No kids allowed so rather quiet. Staff are friendly and keen to help you. Pool, spa and everything else you could want. Changing rooms and studio for yoga are spot on.

CRAYFORD Crayside Leisure Centre *Stadium Way, Crayford, Kent DA1. Tel: 01322 528159 www.geocities.com/*

crayside Near the local dog track so you could always place a bet after your yoga class. Facilities here are on a small scale. A lot of activities on offer but the limited facilities and the quality of them are a drawback. Apparently Bexley Council are on the way to refurbishment at many of their places so perhaps things here will change. Concentrate on the yoga when you go and never mind the tiled floor.

DARTFORD Reynolds Health Centre *Dartford, Kent DA1. Tel: 01322 277200* This operation is opening new premises very soon and expects to offer yoga. We have no idea what the facilities will be like – but go by and have a look. Sometimes new premises mean a good programme development and any new equipment should be spot on.

DARTFORD St Albans School Hall *St Albans Road, Dartford, Kent DA1. Tel: 01322 287911 jan_forsyth@yahoo.co.uk*

DEAL Viniyoga *Deal, Kent. Tel: 01732 353804* Contact Pamela Tyson

DOVER Dover Leisure Centre & Swimming Pool *Woolcomber Street, Kent CT16. Tel: 01304 201145 reception/225050 gym direct* Book-in-advance yoga classes. Gym, workout class, badminton, squash, pool, sauna and steam room. Café and restaurant.

EDENBRIDGE Edenbridge Leisure Centre *Station Road, Edenbridge, Kent TN8. Tel: 01732 865665* Swimming and teaching pools. Squash and tennis, gym, sauna. The yoga classes are taught in slow movements and for relaxation. Café during the day and bar at night.

ERITH Erith Sports Centre & Olympia Fitness Studio *Avenue Road, Erith, Kent DA8. Tel: 01322 350271 www. leisurelink.u.com* Track, fitness studio, ball courts, tennis – the lot on offer here. You could work out a good fitness programme, making a yoga class the heart of it.

FAVERSHAM Syndale Park Sports & Leisure Centre *London Road, Ospringe, Faversham, Kent ME13 Tel: 01795 591271 tom@syndalepark.force9.co.uk www.syndalepark. force9.co.uk* All levels of yoga taught here. No pool, but there is a gym, aerobics, sauna, jacuzzi and a beauty and aromatherapy suite. More facilities are available nearby in an associated centre, The Coachhouse.

FAWKHAM Fredericks Health & Leisure Club *Brands Hatch Road, Fawkham, Kent DA3. Tel: 01474 872530* Good range of facilities here with regular yoga class plus pool, gym, squash, tennis, snooker, sauna, steam room and jacuzzi. Beautician and personal training available. Crèche.

FOLKESTONE Firs Fitness Club *Firs Lane, Cheriton, Folkestone, Kent CT19. Tel: 01303 270850 info@firsclub.co.uk www.firsclub.co.uk* One of the best! Yoga, stretch and relax, gym, squash, and you don't need to be a member. Restaurant and bar.

FOLKESTONE Folkestone Sports Centre *Radnor Park Avenue, Folkestone, Kent CT19. Tel: 01303 850222* Another great place. Fitness studio, Hatha yoga course, gym, sauna, steam room, sunbeds, jacuzzi. Pool, racquet sports – and golf and skiing. Café.

GILLINGHAM Black Lion Leisure Centre *Definitions Fitness Suite, Mill Road, Gillingham, Kent ME7. Tel: 01634 283703* Weekly yoga classes plus pilates. Pool. Badminton, squash and short tennis. Spa.

GRAVESEND Cascades Leisure Centre *Health Suite, Thong Lane, Gravesend, Kent DA12. Tel: 01474 337471* A great pool complex for both adults and children. Badminton and squash, sauna, steam room, jacuzzi, spa, sunbeds. Crèche. Café.

GRAVESEND Cygnet Leisure Centre *Old Perry Street,*

Northfleet, Gravesend, Kent DA11. Tel: 01474 337485 Yoga classes four times a week at the moment. Pilates on offer too. Pool, gym, fitness suite, squash and badminton, sauna/steam room/sunbeds. Martial arts are taught, including t'ai chi and karate. Café.

GRAVESEND Meopham Leisure Centre Wrotham Road, Meopham, Gravesend, Kent DA13. Tel: 01474 814199 Beginners and intermediates yoga classes – about four different classes each week. Gym, sauna, tennis courts, aerobics available. Neat and to the point.

HERNE BAY Pier Sports Centre Central Parade, Herne Bay, Kent CT6. Tel: 01227 366921 Three levels of yoga classes – beginners, intermediate and advanced – with some five classes running every week. Aerobics and spinning also on offer. Three dance studios, which is great, plus a gym, roller-skating, badminton, squash, table tennis and a nearby pool. Daytime café. One of the better places to get you started with yoga and to keep you fit.

MAIDSTONE David Lloyd Leisure Club 3 Broadway Centre, Maidstone, Kent ME16. Tel: 01622 607605 www.david lloydleisure.co.uk Another of the best! Hatha yoga plus more. Pool, class studio, gym, health and beauty salon, sauna, steam room, jacuzzi. Restaurant and bar.

MAIDSTONE Hatha Yoga Classes Maidstone, Kent ME16. Tel: 01622 715576 rms@globalnet.co.uk

MAIDSTONE Maidstone Leisure Centre Mote Park, Maidstone, Kent ME15. Tel: 01622 761111 Yoga classes for beginners and intermediates. Body balance/t'ai chi/ pilates mixture. Pool, gym, aerobics classes, badminton. Food available. We liked it.

MAIDSTONE Old Rectory Health & Fitness Club The Old Rectory, Farleigh Lane, Maidstone, Kent ME16. Tel: 01622 727779

Eleven-acre site with an outdoor running track. On offer are personalised fitness programmes after an assessment, a gym, pool, sauna, steam room and jacuzzi. There are yoga classes but the programme for other courses is presently limited.

ORPINGTON Darrick Wood School *Lovibonds Avenue, Orpington, Kent BR6. Tel: 01689 860522* Best known for swimming activities, there are still lots of other things going on here, from yoga classes to pilates, martial arts, dance and so on.

ORPINGTON Dragons Health Club *Sandy Lane, St Paul's Cray, Orpington, Kent BR6. Tel: 01689 874884 www.dragons. co.uk* Comprehensive facilities and wide range of activities including yoga sessions. Friendly and family orientated.

ORPINGTON The Priory Leisure Centre *Tintagel Road, Orpington, Kent BR6. Tel: 01689 897793* Attached to a school so classes are normally scheduled for after school hours or weekends.

ORPINGTON The Walnuts Leisure Centre *Lynch Gate Road, Orpington, Kent BR6. Tel: 01689 870533* Go shopping first at the centre nearby and then relax into your yoga class. Good facilities.

ROCHESTER Esporta Health & Fitness *Chariot Way, Rochester, Kent ME22. Tel: 01634 292929 www.esporta.com* All you could ask for including three therapists in a health and beauty suite. Hatha yoga classes plus a general yoga course. The programme offers more than 40 classes each week of different disciplines so check it out. Pool, gym, sauna, steam room and jacuzzi. Restaurant and bar.

ROCHESTER Hundred of Hoo Sports Centre *Main Road, Hoo, Rochester, Kent ME3. Tel: 01634 251588* Different teachers at different times for the yoga classes. Best to go along and talk to them. Pool, squash courts and beautician on offer.

ROCHESTER Moores Health & Fitness Club *671*

Maidstone Road, Rochester, Kent ME1. Tel: 01634 400003 Many different levels of yoga teaching and classes are held four times a week. There is also a pilates class. Facilities include gym, pool, health spa, sauna, steam room and jacuzzi. Sunbeds too.

ROCHESTER Strood Sports Centre *Watling Street, Rochester, Kent ME2. Tel: 01634 723888* All-levels general yoga classes plus aerobics. Nice pool, gym, sauna, steam room, jacuzzi, and a health and beauty suite on site. Yoga is a separate operation so you need to enquire about how to book.

SEVENOAKS Iyengar Yoga *Sevenoaks, Kent TN13. Tel: 01959 532339 katy.taylor@lineone.net*

SEVENOAKS Raleys Gym *Plymouth Drive, Sevenoaks, Kent TN13. Tel: 01732 458614* Hatha yoga, pilates, t'ai chi – all about £5 a session. A no-frills place with very limited facilities, but friendly and welcoming.

SHEERNESS Harpers Fitness *Sheppey Leisure Complex, Off the Broadway, Sheerness, Kent ME12. Tel: 01795 668061 sheppey@leisureconnection.co.uk www.harpersfitness.co.uk* You can turn up for most of the classes here but pilates needs to be booked. Yoga and Power Chi. Aerobics, indoor football, badminton and squash, pool across the road, gym. Alternative therapists including reflexologist are available on site by arrangement. Café.

SIDCUP David Lloyd Leisure Club *Baugh Road, Sidcup, Kent DA14. Tel: 020 8309 4949 www.davidlloydleisure.co.uk* Busy, bubbling, glad-to-see-you place. Loads going on here. Different levels of yoga teaching – but it's popular so book early. Studio with over 50 classes on offer including pilates. Two pools – indoor and outdoor. Gym, tennis, squash, outdoor courts. Sauna, steam room, jacuzzi. They will design and organise a personal fitness programme for you. Bar.

SITTINGBOURNE Harpers Fitness Club *Swallows Leisure Centre, Central Avenue, Sittingbourne, Kent ME10. Tel: 01795 421421 swallows@leisureconnection.co.uk www.harpersfitness. co.uk* 35 different classes on offer including yoga. Pilates, ever popular, has got a waiting list. There is a pool, gym and sunbeds. Nice place.

SWANLEY White Oak Leisure Centre *Hilda May Avenue, Swanley, Kent BR8. Tel: 01322 663827* No frills but everything you need in one place including yoga and pilates, a pool, gym, aerobics, beauty therapist, crèche and café. Look no further – White Oak Centre will do.

SWANSCOMBE Swanscombe Leisure Centre *Craylands Lane, Swanscombe, Kent DA10. Tel: 01322 385183* The basics – yoga class, aerobics, small gym and a bar.

TENTERDEN Tenterden Leisure Centre *Recreation Ground Road, Tenterden, Kent TN30. Tel: 01580 765987* Two yoga classes a week. Health and relaxation emphasis here with pilates class, pool, sauna and spa, solarium, beauty therapist. Crèche. Café.

TONBRIDGE Angel Leisure Centre *Angel Lane, Tonbridge, Kent TN9. Tel: 01732 359588* Yoga classes four times a week, mornings and evenings. Facilities include fitness suite, use of nearby pool, aerobics, gym, badminton and short tennis.

TONBRIDGE Hunters Health & Fitness Ltd *2–12 Avebury Avenue, Tonbridge, Kent TN9. Tel: 01732 773512* General yoga during school term-time and you pay class by class. Gym, sauna, steam room, aerobics and, for those who are game, a belly-dancing class. Try it – it's fun.

TONBRIDGE Putlands Sports & Leisure Centre *Mascalls Court Road, Paddock Wood, Tonbridge, Kent TN12. Tel: 01892 838290* More a health club facility than a sports centre, this place is very busy and popular, with six weekly yoga courses. There is a waiting list so hurry up! Beginners and intermediate yoga. Gym, aerobics and sunbed plus a health and beauty therapist on site. We liked it.

TUNBRIDGE WELLS Victoria Health Club *4 Market Square, Royal Victoria Place, Tunbridge Wells, Kent TN1. Tel: 01892 513444* Member of the LA Fitness leisure group so membership is necessary. Beginners and intermediate yoga classes plus lots of other classes. Excellent facilities with a gym, cardio suite, pool, sauna, steam room and sunbeds, and various therapists available including beautician and osteopath.

TUNBRIDGE WELLS Westborough Sports Centre *Oakwood Park, Tunbridge Wells, Kent ME16. Tel: 01622 759615* Football, squash courts, gymnastics and a gym, pool in the future – everything active and busy with great plans for further development. OK, it's your basics now but the town council has big plans. Watch this space! Meanwhile, go to the general yoga class here.

WEST MALLING Inner Light Yoga & Health Company *West Malling, Kent ME20. Tel: 01622 715576 rms@ globalnet.co.uk* Hatha yoga classes by qualified British Wheel of Yoga teacher. Beginners and intermediates. Classes also held in Aylesford and Maidstone.

WEST MALLING Kings Hill Centre *70 Gibson Drive, Kings Hill, West Malling, Kent ME19. Tel: 01732 849656 cuddon@btopenworld.com* Contact Monica Cuddon for details of classes, which include ones for beginners.

MIDDLESEX

GENERAL Yoga-dham *Middlesex. Tel: 020 8428 6691* Contact Tara Patel

BRENTFORD Brentford Fountain Leisure Centre *658 Chiswick High Road, Brentford, Middlesex TW8. Tel: 020 8994 6901 www.cip.org.uk* Three pool areas. Family orientated. Excellent Life Centre gym. Not as up to date in some areas as it ought to be, but a wide range of activities and classes including yoga.

ENFIELD Albany Pool *505 Enfield Road, Enfield, Middlesex EN1. Tel: 020 8804 4255* Yoga plus two pools, one for teaching. All ages and levels catered for here.

GREENFORD Boots Wellbeing Centre *Westway Cross Retail Park, Greenford, Middlesex UB6. Tel: 0845 121 9000 www.wellbeing.com* A pleasant place for yoga with loads of facilities and staff to take care of you, ranging from nurses to an osteopath. Crèche.

HANWORTH Feltham Airparcs Leisure Centre *Uxbridge Road, Hanworth, Middlesex TW13. Tel: 020 8894 9156 www.cip.org.uk* One of the better leisure centres in the area. Yoga and lots of other things to do.

HARROW Fitz Club *14 Havelock Place, Harrow, Middlesex HA2. Tel: 020 8861 2412 www.fitzclub.co.uk* In the heart of Harrow. Everything you need is on offer here. Plenty of classes in a bright studio.

HAYES Pegasus Health Spa *Radisson Edwardian Hotels, 140 Bath Road, Hayes, Middlesex UB3. Tel: 020 8817 2606* Usual gym stuff and a lovely spa pool. Yoga classes usually on offer.

HOUNSLOW Renaissance London Heathrow Hotel Health Club *Bath Road, Hounslow, Middlesex TW3. Tel: 020 8564 6162*

HOUNSLOW Yoga Shakti Mission Trust *Hounslow Yoga Centre, 74–76 Hibernia Road, Middlesex TW3. Tel: 020 8572 8273 www.yogashakti.co info@yogashakti.co* Ma Yoga Shakti teaching with occasional visits from the teacher Mataji, who gives course intensives. Ask for full programme of yoga classes. Nearest tube Hounslow (Central Line) or Hounslow mainline station.

ISLEWORTH Isleworth Recreation Centre *Twickenham Road, Isleworth, Middlesex TW7. Tel: 020 8560 6855* Smart swimming pools. Not the greatest gym and facilities, but OK. Small studio. Friendly and helpful staff.

NORTHOLT Dragons Health Club *Rowdell Road, Northolt, Middlesex UB5. Tel: 020 8841 5611 www.dragons.co.uk* Full facilities here but a touch on the well-used side. Lots of classes including yoga but you might have to pay extra after joining for some of the sessions. Ask what you get for your membership fee.

NORTHWOOD Dragons Health & Fitness Club *Chestnut Avenue, Northwood, Middlesex HA6. Tel: 01923 822000 www.dragons.co.uk* Not much to complain about here – everything you will need in a friendly if businesslike atmosphere.

OSTERLEY Jealous Health Club *8 Windmill Avenue, Osterley, Middlesex TW7. Tel: 020 8893 6882* Wonderful swimming pool and ample facilities. Regular yoga classes. We love the name.

PINNER The Grail Community *125 Waxwell Lane, Pinner, Middlesex HA5. Tel: 020 8866 2195/0505 waxwell@ compuserve.com* One of several branches of the Grail Society, which was founded in Holland in 1921, the Grail Community at Pinner is a Roman Catholic institute for married and single people. The household here is run by single women. It has a Christian focus but all are welcome. Yoga is offered along with a number of other workshops and courses including weaving, spinning, prayer, healing and just relaxing. A comfortable atmosphere with good hospitality.

RUISLIP Highgrove Pool *Eastcote Road, Ruislip, Middlesex HA4. Tel: 01895 632544* Pool and leisure centre with gym upstairs and classes including yoga.

SOUTHALL Dormers Wells Leisure Centre *Dormers Wells Lane, Southall, Middlesex UB1. Tel: 020 8571 7207* Yoga and lots of other activities including pool, personal training, stretch area and sports hall.

SOUTHALL Featherstone Sports Centre *Montague Way, Southall, Middlesex UB1. Tel: 020 8813 9886* Managed by the nearby secondary school, this place is in a much-needed process of transformation to update it. Yoga continues to be on offer so check out the refurbished facilities.

STANMORE Aspire National Training Centre *Wood Lane, Stanmore, Middlesex HA7. Tel: 020 8954 5759 www. aspire.org.uk* Caters for both disabled and able-bodied clients in a totally integrated atmosphere. Clean and well maintained with friendly staff. Regular yoga classes. Try it.

SUDBURY Vale Farm Sports Centre *Watford Road, Sudbury, Middlesex HA0. Tel: 020 8908 6545 www.leisurecon- nection.co.uk* A great modern centre with all you could ask for in one place, including good yoga classes. Beginners to advanced. Bar. Café. OK, we like it!

UXBRIDGE Brunel University Sports Centre *Kingston Lane, Uxbridge, Middlesex UB8. Tel: 01895 203305* All-weather, all-sports site. Huge programme on offer including yoga. Regular refurbishment upgrades. Check it out.

UXBRIDGE Flex Health Club *Stage Door, 233 High Street, Uxbridge, Middlesex UB8. Tel: 01895 271217 www.flex.uk.net* A four-level facility. Friendly male–female client balance. Bright, clean and offers yoga.

UXBRIDGE Virgin Active *The Arena Club, Stockley Park, Uxbridge, Middlesex UB11. Tel: 0845 130 1777 www.virgin.*

com/active Two floors of facilities. Good equipment. A lot on offer here including yoga. Café. Crèche

SURREY

CAMBERLEY British Wheel of Yoga & Bihar School of Yoga *Glenbarry, 53 Blackdown Road, Deepcut, Camberley, Surrey GU16. Tel: 01252 834240 kate@yogasankhya. freeserve.co.uk*

CAMBERLEY Heatherside Yoga *Martindale Avenue, Heatherside, Camberley, Surrey GU15. Tel: 01276 506369 gillian-m-bex@hotmail.com www.yogaclass.net* Mixed abilities. Beginners welcome. Twice-weekly class. When you telephone the above number, ask for Rosie to get all the details.

CAMBERLEY Tekels Park Guest House *Tekels Park, Camberley, Surrey GU15. Tel: 01276 23159 ghouse.tekels@ btclick.com* Tekels Park is owned by the Theosophical Society in England and the programme on offer may include these kind of events in addition to yoga and meditation: Mayan Mysteries, The Sacred Circle, New Aspects of Space & Time, The Rebirthing Experience, and Dancing the Sevenfold Energies of Life. The guesthouse, which is set in over 50 acres of secluded woods and fields, has earned a reputation for serving excellent vegetarian food. Open all year. Single and double rooms available. Facilities: camping, garden, park, library, guest lounge, TV, payphone. Healing courses available. Meals: guests eat together. Vegetarian and wholefood. Special diets catered for. Bookings: letter or telephone. Access: by rail or car.

CARSHALTON Westcroft Leisure Centre *Westcroft Road, Carshalton, Surrey SM5. Tel: 020 8770 4847 www.scl98. com* High on racquet sports here and low on classes and courses – but yoga is going at the moment. Pool, gym, badminton, squash, softball, tennis, table tennis, pool and gym. Café and bar.

CHERTSEY Health & Beauty at Foxhills *Foxhills Lodge, Stonehill Road, Ottershaw, Chertsey, Surrey KT16. Tel: 01932 704460* Gym, pool, twelve tennis courts (count them!), a modest three squash courts, hair and beauty salon, sauna and steam room. Hatha yoga classes. Crèche. Café for lunch.

CHESSINGTON Chessington Sports Centre *Garrison Lane, Chessington, Surrey KT9. Tel: 020 8974 2277 www. kingston.gov.uk* Yoga is sometimes on offer here so check out what is current. Facility OK.

CLAYGATE Claygate Village Hall *Church Road, Claygate, Surrey KT10. Tel: 01372 469221* British Wheel of Yoga qualified teacher for mixed-ability classes.

CRANLEIGH Cranleigh Leisure Centre *Village Way, Cranleigh, Surrey GU6. Tel: 01483 274400 www.waverley. gov.uk/sports/cran_home.html* Good classes – yoga, pilates and t'ai chi plus a body balance class. Usual facilities including gym, pool, relaxation area, sauna, steam room and jacuzzi. Crèche. Café.

CROYDON Addington Palace Country Club *Gravel Hill, Addington Village, Croydon, Surrey CR0. Tel: 020 8662 5050* A wide range of natural therapies on offer as well as yoga and training. All this in an eighteenth-century mansion where luxury and relaxation are keynotes.

CROYDON CJ's Gym, Fitness & Martial Arts Centre *33 Lower Coombe Street, Croydon, Surrey CR0. Tel: 020 8680 0693* Exercise and fitness plus martial arts and yoga in a large studio, plus classes for kids.

CROYDON Dragons Health Club *33 Imperial Way, Croydon, Surrey CR0. Tel: 020 8686 8811 www.dragons.co.uk*

Friendly and recently updated. With three squash courts, a pool, gym, sauna and steam room, crèche and bar, it goes without saying that there is yoga (three times a week).

CROYDON Greens Health & Fitness *1 Colonnades, 619 Purley Way, Croydon CR0. Tel: 020 8680 2228 www. greensonline.co.uk* Natural light, great space, purpose-built and impressive range of facilities on offer. Good social scene particularly for the slightly older age group. Yoga is very popular here.

CROYDON LivingWell Health Club *Waddon Way, Off Purley Way, Croydon, Surrey CR9. Tel: 020 8667 4444 www. livingwell.co.uk* Basic place – yoga class, pool, sauna, steam room and jacuzzi.

CROYDON Selsdon Park Hotel Leisure Club *Addington Road, Sanderstead, South Croydon, Surrey CR2. Tel: 020 8657 8811* Over 200 acres of surrounding parkland and attachment to the grand Selsdon Park Hotel. You name it, they got it. Spoiled for choice with your yoga class in an outstanding facility.

EPSOM Dragons Health & Fitness Club *27 Ruxley Lane, Epsom, Surrey KT19. Tel: 020 8393 6011 www.dragons.co.uk* Dragons everywhere you look! Yoga classes, pool, gym, sauna, jacuzzi, beauty therapist, crèche and café. Nice one, Dragon!

EPSOM Ruth White Yoga Centre *99 College Road, Epsom, Surrey KT17. Tel: 020 8644 0309 www.ruthwhiteyoga.com* Retreats are usually at the weekends but there are also four-day breaks and a summer holiday. Facilities include camping, garden and guest lounge. Wholefood meals taken together. Charges are specific for each event and venue so ask when you book.

FARNHAM Farnham Sports Centre Yoga Group *Witley, Surrey GU8. Tel: 01483 422655* Contact Sarah Ball

FARNHAM Farnham Sports Centre *Dogflud Way, Farnham, Surrey GU9. Tel: 01252 723208 www.waverley.gov.uk/sports/farn_home.htm* Spoiled for choice with the classes here. Beginners and improvers yoga plus Power yoga and a general yoga class. Pool, badminton, table tennis, squash. Beautician available by appointment. Crèche. Sandwiches and coffee.

GODALMING The Barn *Wiggins Yard, Bridge Street, Godalming, Surrey GU7. Tel: 01483 418103 tony.palmer@ntlworld.com* Hatha yoga and yoga for relaxation classes.

GODALMING Godalming Students' Association *Tel: 01483 417428* Contact Mrs J. Milner

GODALMING Satya Yoga *Godalming. Tel: 01483 419601* Contact Sandra Billinge

GRAYSHOTT Grayshott Hall *Headley Road, Grayshott, Hindhead, Surrey GU26. Tel: 01428 604331 www.grayshotthall.com* Famous place with a continually high reputation and all you would expect to find in a well-established health resort. Yoga and other classes throughout the day every day, as there are residential guests on fitness and health programmes. Pool, gym, tennis and golf. Food is good and very healthy. You might want to come here for a three-day retreat and make yoga the focus of your stay, combined with a quality workout and exercise programme.

GRAYSHOTT Yoga with Josephine *Ludshott House, Grayshott, Surrey GU26. Tel: 01428 604898 jchiover@aol.com* One-to-one yoga sessions only. Specialises in yoga for asthma and lower back problems.

GUILDFORD Dragons Health & Fitness *Epsom Road, Guildford, Surrey GU4. Tel: 01483 458811 www.dragons.co.uk* Members only so go in and have a look before you join. One of a very good chain of leisure centres – lots of yoga every week, pool, gym, bar and more.

GUILDFORD Forte Spa Health & Fitness Club *Egerton Road, Guildford, Surrey GU2. Tel: 01483 453134* This club is part of a hotel so you can eat here after your class. Yoga on offer along with a pool, gym, jacuzzi, sauna, steam room and studio. No racquet sports. Beauty therapist can be arranged. Hotel clubs can be OK and are rarely busy – but some facilities are less than spacious.

HASLEMERE Herons Swimming & Fitness Centre *Kings Road, Haslemere, Surrey GU27. Tel: 01428 658484 www.waverley.gov.uk/sports/herons_home.html* Yoga classes. Aerobics and workouts. Sauna and steam room. Jacuzzi. Crèche. Café.

HORLEY Horley Anderson Centre *Thornton Close, Court Lodge Estate, Horley, Surrey RH6. Tel: 01293 784075* Two pools, gym, health suite, yoga and exercise classes. Your basic unit.

KINGSTON Holmes Place Health Club *3rd Floor Bentalls, Wood Street, Kingston-upon-Thames, Surrey KT1. Tel: 020 8549 7700 www.holmesplace.co.uk* Pool, aerobics, massages, yoga every day.

KINGSTON Kingfisher Leisure Centre *Fairfield Road, Kingston-upon-Thames, Surrey KT1. Tel: 020 8546 1042 www.dcleisure.co.uk* Beginners yoga and mixed-ability classes too. Nice pool, gym, circuit training, aerobics, steam room, jacuzzi. Crèche. Café. Family orientated. Lots to do. Fully equipped place. Yoga in the dance studio.

KINGSTON Kingsmeadow Athletic & Fitness Centre *422A Kingston Road, Kingston-upon-Thames, Surrey KT1. Tel: 020 8547 2198* Small leisure centre offering yoga classes.

KINGSTON Kingston YMCA Health & Fitness Club *49 Victoria Road, Surbiton, Surrey KT6. Tel: 020 8399 5427* A small place trying to reform itself and what it has to offer.

Check out the current programme to see if yoga is running.

KINGSTON LA Fitness *161 Clarence Street, Kingston-upon-Thames, Surrey KT1. Tel: 020 8547 0970 www.lafitness.co.uk* All levels of yoga on offer. Gym, aerobics, sunbeds, steam room, a ladies-only gym. Internet café, which is rather rare in the clubs we have listed – perhaps a need in the future if customers are going to spend a long time there. Text messages and mail, like life, always roll on.

KINGSTON YMCA Hawker Leisure *Lower Ham Road, Kingston-upon-Thames, Surrey KT1. Tel: 020 8296 9747* Thoroughly modern and up-to-the minute place. It's near the river, so you could take a picnic.

KINGSTON The Yoga Practice *United Reformed Church, Eden Street, Kingston-upon-Thames, Surrey KT1. Tel: 07775 900020 turiya@yogamatters.fsnet.co.uk* Mixed-ability classes including a weekly more advanced class. Rate is usually by session.

LIGHTWATER Lightwater Leisure Centre *Lightwater Country Park, The Avenue, Lightwater, Surrey GU18. Tel: 01276 472662* Basic and Astanga yoga offered. Gym, sports hall with squash, tennis and short tennis, football, sauna and sunbeds. Bar.

LONG DITTON Long Ditton Yoga Centre *25 Effingham Road, Long Ditton, Surrey KT6. Tel: 020 8398 1741 richardsjudith@hotmail.com* Iyengar yoga classes with Judith Richards.

MITCHAM Lavender Park & College Pavilion *Lavender Avenue, Mitcham, Surrey CR4. Tel: 020 8646 7362 www.merton.gov.uk* Basic gym and sports hall. Limited facilities but yoga usually on offer.

NEW MALDEN Maiden Centre *Blagdon Road, New Malden, Surrey KT3. Tel: 020 8547 6601* Pool and many activities on offer here including regular yoga. Café. Crèche.

OXTED Pandridge Leisure Pool *Hoskins Road, Oxted, Surrey RH8. Tel: 01883 722811* General, beginners and intermediate yoga classes. Pool, play pool, gym, sauna, steam room and whirlpool. Crèche. Bar with some food.

REDHILL Donyngs Recreation Centre *Linkfield Lane, Redhill, Surrey RH1. Tel: 01737 764732* Friendly place with yoga classes, pool, gym, health suite, badminton and squash. Crèche. Café.

REDHILL Priory Health & Leisure Club *Nutfield Priory, Nutfield Road, Redhill, Surrey RH1. Tel: 01737 823510* Beginners and intermediate yoga classes plus a pool, gym, sauna, steam room, jacuzzi and two squash courts. Crèche. Bar.

REDHILL YMCA *Princes Road, Redhill, Surrey RH1. Tel: 01737 779979* We find it hard to fault this or other YMCA facilities. Whether it offers basic or outstanding facilities, each one always has a great atmosphere. This one in Redhill is fairly basic but it holds Hatha yoga classes. A gym and other classes are also available. Crèche. Drinks machine.

RICHMOND-UPON-THAMES Cedars Health Club *Richmond Hill Hotel, Richmond, Surrey TW10. Tel: 020 8332 1010* General yoga. Facilities include gym, pool, sauna, steam room, kids' pool and beauty salon. Café and bar.

RICHMOND-UPON-THAMES Pinnacle Richmond Town *Richmond Athletic Ground, Kewfoot Road, Richmond, Surrey TW9. Tel: 020 8332 7185* Yoga and pilates classes. Gym, squash, sunbeds and a studio for exercise classes. Café and bar. It'll do.

RICHMOND-UPON-THAMES Pools on the Park *Old Deer Park, Twickenham Road, Richmond, Surrey TW9. Tel: 020 8940 0561* Now here's a place to make a splash! One small pool and two big pools. Gym, tennis courts, sauna, steam room and jacuzzi. Osteopath on site plus relaxing and sports massages. Yoga classes are offered on most days, ranging in levels from dynamic yoga to starter yoga courses. We liked this place a lot.

RICHMOND-UPON-THAMES Richmond Hill Health Club *Lewis Road, Richmond, Surrey SW14. Tel: 020 8948 5523 www.fit4ever.co.uk* No pool but good membership rates.

RICHMOND-UPON-THAMES Shene Sports & Fitness Centre *Hertford Avenue, Richmond, Surrey SW14. Tel: 020 8878 7107* Dual use with schools, so opening times can be difficult for the public.

RICHMOND-UPON-THAMES Studioflex *26 Priests Bridge, Richmond, Surrey SW14. Tel: 020 8878 0556* A dance studio with yoga and fitness classes. If yoga is not enough for you, enrol in the belly-dancing.

SANDOWN Sandown Sports Club Limited *Sandown Park, More Lane, Esher, Surrey KT10. Tel: 01372 467133 sandown@sandownsports.co.uk www.sandownsports.co.uk* A dry ski run is the feature here but there is also a gym, squash court, sauna and yoga classes. Bar.

SURBITON Tolworth Recreation Centre *Fullers Way North, Surbiton, Surrey KT6. Tel: 020 8391 7910* Mixed-ability, beginners and intermediate yoga classes. Squash, badminton, table tennis, gym, aerobics studio, health suite, after-school activities for kids, trampolining. Café and bar.

SUTTON Cheam Leisure Centre *Malden Road, Sutton, Surrey SM3. Tel: 020 8770 4830 www.scl98.com* Get-to-the-point and get-fit place – yoga twice a week at the moment plus gym, pool, sauna, steam room, sunbeds and squash.

SUTTON Fit Stop Wellness Centre *St Nicholas Road,*

Sutton, Surrey SM3. Tel: 020 8770 3535 Situated in the centre of town, this down-to-earth place is good for a quick work-out or yoga class.

SUTTON Pinnacle Sutton & Cheam Club *Gander Green Lane, Sutton, Surrey SM1. Tel: 020 8642 6888* Yoga classes. Three squash courts, gym, crèche, bar.

SUTTON Surrey Iyengar Yoga Centre *Cheam, Sutton, Surrey SM3. Tel: 020 8644 0309* Contact Ruth White

SUTTON The Zone *Rose Hill Park, Sutton, Surrey SM3. Tel: 020 8641 8343 www.sjtc.org* In the middle of a park. Well-qualified staff and OK facilites. Yoga on offer.

TADWORTH Banstead Sports Centre *Merland Rise, Tadworth, Surrey KT20. Tel: 01737 361933 jo.clark@courtneys.co.uk www.courtneys.co.uk* We like this place, with its big pool, gym, two studios, squash, tennis and health suite with sauna. Yoga classes. Crèche. Café.

THAMES DITTON Colets Health & Fitness *Off Speer Road, Thames Ditton, Surrey KT7. Tel: 020 8398 1858* Five yoga classes a week now running. Big pool, workout studio, gym, six squash courts, hairdresser and beauty treatments. Café/bar.

WALTON-ON-THAMES Elmbridge Leisure Centre *Waterside Drive, Walton-on-Thames, Surrey KT12. Tel: 01932 243863* No pool on site but one five minutes down the road – a little walk is good for you after your yoga class. Gym, squash, aerobics, badminton, sauna. Crèche. Café.

WINDLESHAM Yoga Seekers *Thorncombe, Church Road, Windlesham, Surrey GU20. Tel: 01276 473371* Swami Satyaratnananda holds regular classes.

WITLEY Witley Yoga Group *Witley. Tel: 01448 3422655* Contact Sarah Ball

WOKING Chekira Wholistic Trust *Yoga & Therapy Centre,*

*Beech Lawn, Beech Grove, Mayford, Woking, Surrey GU22. Tel:
01483 870064* The Chekira Wholistic Trust is a training centre
for the Friends of Yoga Society International and is affiliated
to the Institute for Complementary Medicine. The Trust
provides teacher-training courses, teacher supply and
support, weekend yoga workshops, weekly yoga classes,
private one-to-one tuition, and certain complementary therapies. The director of the Chekira Trust is Brenda Brown,
who has been teaching yoga for over 30 years. She and her
team of qualified yoga teachers and therapists work throughout Surrey and the surrounding areas.

WOKING Maybury Centre *Woking. Tel: 01483 724065*
Contact Riny van Akkeren

WOKING Peak Fitness *51 Chertsey Road, Woking,
Surrey GU21. Tel: 01483 814131 tony.palmer@ntlworld.com*
Beginners and general yoga classes and courses.

WOKING Woking & District Yoga Club *Chobham. Tel:
01276 858884* Contact Ralph Gabriel

WOKING Woking Leisure Centre Yoga Club *Woking. Tel:
01483 747519* Contact Brenda Brown

SUSSEX

GENERAL East Sussex Yoga Teachers & Classes
www.yoga4health.biz/eastsussex.asp

Institute of Iyengar Yoga (Sussex Branch) *www.iiya.org.uk*

Viniyoga in Sussex *Tel: 01293 536664* Contact Gill Lloyd

BATTLE Patanjali Yoga Centre & Ashram *Battle, Sussex.
Tel: 01424 870538* Contact Sri Indar Nath

BRIGHTON Yoga Plus *177 Ditchling Road, Brighton,
Sussex BN1. Tel: 01273 276175 www.yogaplus.co.uk* Yoga Plus
specialise in Astanga Vinyasa yoga.

CRAWLEY Worth Abbey *Paddockhurst Road, Turners Hill,*

Crawley, West Sussex RH10. Tel: 01342 710310 Education and pastoral work are the business of this community. The setting is beautiful. Guest accommodation has been recently expanded and there is now a full programme of events on offer. Open all year except July and August. Facilities include camping, garden, guest lounge. Children welcomed. Chapel, choir. Everyone eats together. Traditional food. Vegetarians and special diets catered for. Guests are welcome to attend Divine Office as well as Mass. Access: train from Victoria station to Three Bridges. Car via M23, Exit 10 to East Grinstead.

CROWBOROUGH Hourne Farm Centre for Yoga *Crowborough. Tel: 01892 661093* Contact Peter Randel

HASTINGS Croft Road Yoga *Croft Road, Hastings, Sussex TN34. Tel: 01424 753502*

HASTINGS Hastings & District Yoga Association *Tel: 01424 434400* Contact Ken Bennett

HASTINGS Horntype Park *Hastings, Sussex TN34. Tel: 01424 753502*

HASTINGS Red Cross Hall Yoga *Red Cross Hall, Hastings, Sussex TN34. Tel: 01424 753502*

HOVE Bikram Yoga Brighton & Hove *Old Perfume Factory, Fonthill Road (just behind Hove train station), Sussex BN3. Tel: 01273 721944 bikramyogabrightonandhove@hotmail.com www.bikramyoga.com* Regular classes during the week. The attitude here is warm and friendly and this is what they tell you: 'Bring a large towel, water, empty stomach, sense of humour and a mat.'

HOVE Cornerstone Community Centre *Church Road, Hove, Sussex BN3. Tel: 01273 735372* A very special yoga class and course for those who suffer from ME. You pay by the hour and it is held on a regular basis.

NEWHAVEN Meeching Hall *South Road, Newhaven, Sussex BN9. Tel: 01273 512306 energisebodywise@lineone.net*

PEACEHAVEN Meridian Community Halls *Meridian Way Co-Op Building, Peacehaven, Sussex BN10. Tel: 01273 512306 energisebodywise@lineone.net*

SEAFORD Seaford Women's Institute *Brooklyn Road, Seaford, Sussex BN25. Tel: 01273 512306* Yoga classes usually on offer here three times a week.

UCKFIELD Yoga for All *Ukfield Civic Centre, Bell Lane, Uckfield, Sussex TN22. Tel: 01825 768010* Breathing and relaxation exercises. All ages and abilities welcomed.

WELLINGLY Yoga for All *Wellshurst Golf & Country Club, Wellingly, Sussex BN27. Tel: 01825 768010* All ages welcomed. Both members and non-members may attend. Beginners encouraged.

WORTHING Bihar School of Yoga *Flat 2, 33 Winchester Road, Worthing, Sussex BN11. Tel: 01903 820525* Contact Swami Ramdevananda

EAST AND EAST ANGLIA

BEDFORDSHIRE

GENERAL Bedfordshire Yoga Association *Tel: 01234 852756.* Contact Ann Davenport

BEDFORD Alexander Sports Centre *De Montford University, Sidney Road, Bedford, Bedfordshire MK40. Tel: 01234 345208* This is the base for a wide range of sports and leisure facilities. There are gyms, sports halls and lots more including regular yoga classes. Easy and friendly place. Lots of students.

BEDFORD Bunyan Sports Centre *Mile Road, Bedford, Bedfordshire MK42. Tel: 01234 364481* Evening yoga class. Very popular and lasts about one and a half hours.

BEDFORD Dragons Health Club *81–83 Kimbolton Road, Bedford, Bedfordshire MK41. Tel: 01234 354363 www.dragons.co.uk* Regular yoga class plus fitness room, pool, aerobics, squash, sunbeds, sauna, bar and café. A complete package of facilities on offer.

BIGGLESWADE Saxon Pool & Leisure Centre *Saxon Drive, Biggleswade, Bedfordshire SG18. Tel: 01767 313190* Pool. Fitness suite. Regular yoga class during the week.

BIGGLESWADE Yoga for Health Foundation *Ickwell Bury, Biggleswade, Bedfordshire SG18. Tel: 01767 627271* See Introduction for details.

BILLINGTON Billington Village Hall *Billington, Bedfordshire HP22. Tel: 01525 210553 yogalison@hotmail.com* Twice-weekly classes which include regular meditation practice.

DUNSTABLE Dunstable Leisure Centre *Court Drive, Dunstable, Bedfordshire LU5. Tel: 01582 604307/01582 608107 dunstable@leisureconnection.co.uk www.leisure*

connection.co.uk Dance and yoga studio. Pool. Gym. Crèche. This is a big centre and popular.

DUNSTABLE R-3 Leisure Club *71–73 High Street North, Dunstable, Bedfordshire LU6. Tel: 01582 477500* Friday morning yoga class in studio. Gym, beauty treatments, steam room and sauna.

HARROLD Harrold Village Hall *Harrold, Bedfordshire MK43. Tel: 01234 720954* Only ten minutes away from Bedford, this small village has yoga classes twice a week. The cost is around £4 a session. Take your own towel to lie on. If you are new to the area, there are two nearby places worth a visit on your way to or from your yoga class. One is the Carlton Emmaus Village, a charity for homeless people who earn their way by recycling all the stuff we don't want and then offering it to new buyers. There is a café and various shops, which sell everything from refurbished household furniture to books. The other place is Turvey Abbey (see entry below for Turvey).

HENLOW Henlow Grange Health Farm *The Grange, Henlow, Bedfordshire SG16. Tel: 01462 811111 enquiries@ henlowgrange.co.uk* Weekly and daily yoga classes in the Mind & Body Studio. A mixed crowd but predominantly female. Pool, fitness room, sauna and bar.

LEIGHTON BUZZARD Greenleas School *Derwent Road, Linslade, Leighton Buzzard, Bedfordshire HP22. Tel: 01525 210553 yogalison@hotmail.com* Weekly yoga class suitable for everyone.

LEIGHTON BUZZARD Marins Health & Leisure Ltd *Leighton Road, Leighton Buzzard, Bedfordshire LU7. Tel: 01525 853000 enquiries@energielifestyle.co.uk* Weekly yoga classes. Gym, sauna, exercise studio.

LEIGHTON BUZZARD Tiddenfoot Leisure Centre

Mentmore Road, Leighton Buzzard, Bedfordshire LU7. Tel: 01525 375765 tiddenfoot@leisureconnection.co.uk Yoga in the aerobic studio. Two pools, gym, dance plus kids' activities. Nice.

LEIGHTON BUZZARD Working Men's Club *Garden Hedge, Leighton Buzzard, Bedfordshire HP22. Tel: 01525 210553 yogalison@hotmail.com* Twice-weekly yoga classes in which all students work at their own level and pace. The keynote here is to remain comfortable and practise yoga within your own individual capacities.

LUTON Dimension Health & Fitness Ltd *The Poynt, Poynters Road, Luton, Bedfordshire LU4. Tel: 01582 493939 Pete.foster@dimensionfitness.com www.dimensionfitness.com* Over 30s crowd here. Regular yoga plus a full range of classes. Gym. Weights room. There is also a slimmers club so one can work out a fitness/yoga plus slimming programme all in one place. Coffee and tea facilities.

LUTON Lea Manor Recreation Centre *Northwell Drive, Luton, Bedfordshire LU3. Tel: 01582 599888* Regular yoga classes. Gym, squash, pool.

LUTON Putteridge Recreation Centre *Putteridge Road, Luton, Bedfordshire LU2. Tel: 01582 731664* Sunday yoga in a large sports room.

MILLBROOK VILLAGE Susan Hill Yoga *(via the Millbrook Golf Club), Millbrook, Near Ampthill, Bedfordshire MK45. Tel: 01525 634873 Sue_yoga@hotmail.com www.sueyoga. freeservers.com* There are three different levels taught in the Millbrook classes – yoga for beginners, intermediates, and a general yoga class. See the Turvey entry below for details of the kind of yoga taught by Susan Hill.

SANDY Potton Sports Centre *Sun Street, Potton, Sandy, Bedfordshire SG19. Tel: 01767 260101 tony@pottonsports* centre.co.uk www.pottonsportscentre.co.uk This place is big on trampolines. Gym and fitness room. Sauna. Regular yoga classes.

TURVEY Susan Hill Yoga *Turvey Lower School, May Road, Turvey, Bedfordshire MK43. Tel: 01525 634873 Sue_yoga@ hotmail.com www.sueyoga.freeservers.com* Both beginners and intermediates are catered for by Susan Hill, who also holds classes in Olney and Millbrook villages. She teaches Iyengar yoga and the exercises are graded to ensure safety from beginner's stage to the advanced practitioner. The old stone village of Turvey is a lovely place, and the nearby Turvey Abbey, home to two communities of nuns and monks, is well worth a visit. A monastery shop sells various small items including hand-painted icons and tiles, cards and spirituality materials for children.

WYBOSTON Harpers Health & Fitness Club *Great North Road, Wyboston, Bedfordshire MK44. Tel: 01480 403233 www.harpersfitness.co.uk* Yoga and pilates. Gym, pool, sauna, steam room, weights, beauty treatments and a crèche.

CAMBRIDGESHIRE

GENERAL

Beverley Nolan *Beverley.nolan@btinternet.com www. btinternet.com/~yoga* Iyengar-style yoga.

Cambridge Iyengar Yoga Centre *59 Norfolk Terrace, Cambridge CB1 info@cambridgeyoga.co.uk*

Parks Physio Centre *Tel: 01767 651644 Jill.Evans@tesco.net* Hatha yoga offered in weekly classes by Jill Evans, a British Wheel of Yoga teacher for twenty years. Diplomas in Aromatherapy and Indian Head Massage.

Yoga Biomedical Trust *Cambridge. Tel: 01223 36730* Contact Dr Robin Monro

Other Iyengar yoga-trained teachers in the Cambridge area:

Pavara *Tel: 01223 353949*

Shaddhasara *Tel: 01223 693842*

ABBOTSLEY Abbotsley Village Hall *Tel: 01767 651644 Jill.Evans@tesco.net* Hatha yoga offered in weekly classes by Jill Evans, a British Wheel of Yoga teacher for twenty years. Diplomas in Aromatherapy and Indian Head Massage.

CAMBRIDGE The Atrium Club *64 Newmarket Road, Cambridge, Cambs CB5. Tel: 01223 522522 atriumclub@ hotmail.com www.atriumclub.com* Yoga class every week. Gym. Sauna plus other good facilities. Café.

CAMBRIDGE Cherry Hinton Village Centre *Colville Road, Cambridge, Cambs CB1. Tel: 01223 576412* Currently offering two evening classes, this centre is really one big sports hall with limited facilities.

CAMBRIDGE Coleridge Community College *Radegund Road, Cambridge, Cambs CB5. Tel: 01223 712540* General Iyengar yoga classes with Penny Lutslawska. Term-time only.

CAMBRIDGE Friends Meeting House *Jesus Lane, Cambridge, Cambs CB5. Tel: 01223 515929* Beginners, drop-in and intermediate Iyengar yoga classes. Term-time only. Contact Sasha Perryman on above telephone number.

CAMBRIDGE Hills Road Sixth Form College *Hills Road, Cambridge, Cambs CB5. Tel: 01223 247251* General Iyengar yoga classes with Penny Lutslawska.

CAMBRIDGE Hills Road Sports & Tennis Centre *Purbeck Road, Cambridge, Cambs CB2 Tel: 01223 500009* Saturdays only for yoga but there are four classes. This centre has loads of things to do – gym, indoor and outdoor tennis courts, squash. Bar open during the week.

CAMBRIDGE Homerton College Dance Studio *Hills*

Road, Cambridge, Cambs CB5 General stretching and relaxation classes are held here, suitable for beginners and experienced students.

CAMBRIDGE Kaetsu Centre *New Hall College, Cambridge, Cambs CB3. Tel: 01223 523410* General Iyengar yoga classes. University term-time only. Contact Philippe Harari on above telephone number.

CAMBRIDGE St Colomba's Hall *Downing Place, Cambridge, Cambs CB5. Tel: 01223 523410* General yoga classes. Contact Philippe Harari on above telephone number or Julia Dale on 01223 360270.

CAMBRIDGE Unitarian Church Hall *Victoria Street, Cambridge, Cambs CB5. Tel: 07799 203489* General Iyengar yoga classes. Contact Louise Dawson on the above telephone number.

CLARE Clare Old School Community Centre *Clare, Suffolk CO10. Tel: 01440 7876228* General Iyengar yoga classes. Contact Jane Perryman on the above telephone number.

ELY The Atrium Club *39 Newnham Street, Ely, Cambs CB7. Tel: 01353 668888 atriumclub@hotmail.com www. atriumclub.com* Intermediate and beginners yoga classes, daytime and evenings. Swimming pool, gym, jacuzzi, sauna, resident beautician, crèche.

ELY Pat Dron *1 Barton Close, Witchford, Ely, Cambs CB6 2HS. Tel: 01353 661023* General, intermediate and improvers Iyengar yoga classes with experienced teacher Pat Dron.

ELY Helen Goodjohn *Tel: 01353 667556 helen@yogaand health.co.uk www.helensyoga.co.uk* Qualified Hatha yoga teacher Helen Goodjohn runs classes in Ely and surrounding areas. Hatha yoga balances mind, body and spirit using stretching, relaxation and breathing techniques. It is suitable for all ages and levels of fitness and Helen has special interests in yoga and asthma and stress in the workplace. She also holds classes in Ely at The Paradise Pool Conference Room, Ely Community College, The Paradise Centre and The Maltings.

ELY Leisure & Sports for Littleport *Camel Road, Littleport, Ely, Cambs CB6. Tel: 01353 860600* Monday evening yoga class. Fitness room plus tennis. Bar.

HADSTOCK Hadstock Village Hall *Near Linton, Cambs CB1. Tel: 01223 890671 jw.henrique@which.net* Yoga and relaxation classes for beginners and the more experienced.

HUNTINGDON Ramsey Sports Centre *Abbey Road, Ramsey, Huntingdon, Cambs PE17. Tel: 01487 710275* Day and evening yoga classes plus gym, sports hall, pool. No bar or café at the minute but the place is being refurbished.

HUNTINGDON St Ivo Recreation Centre *Westwood Road, St Ives, Huntingdon, Cambs PE17. Tel: 01480 388500* St Ivo Recreation Centre runs ten-week yoga courses, usually on a weekday morning. Fitness studio, pool, steam room, sauna, café and bar.

PETERBOROUGH Fitness Zone, *Wentworth Street, Peterborough, Cambs PE1. Tel: 01733 312595* Ladies only here. Full relaxation facilities like saunas and sunbeds. No pool. Weekly yoga classes.

PETERBOROUGH Peterborough Yoga for Health *17 Alexander Road, Peterborough, Cambs PE1. Tel: 01733 310795 delpinofam@apol.com* A weekly general-level yoga class and a monthly Saturday one. Individual tuition, particularly for those with disabilities or chronic health problems. If in doubt about your health, double-check with a second qualified yoga teacher or your doctor before enrolling.

PETERBOROUGH Werrington Sports & Recreation Centre *Staniland Way, Peterborough, Cambs PE4. Tel: 01733*

576606 Evening and weekend yoga classes. There is usually a fee reduction if you sign up for two yoga classes. Facilities include gym, squash, badminton, tennis and karate. No pool or sauna. Bar.

ST NEOTS St Neots Recreation Centre *Barford Road, St Neots, Cambs PE19. Tel: 01480 388700* St Neots Recreation Centre runs a yoga course over twelve weeks at a time. These are popular so you need to get your name down early. There are a lot of facilities to enjoy here – gym, fitness room and classes, sauna and steam room. Bar. Café. Crèche.

Essex

GENERAL

Dharma Yoga Centre *Bassingbourn. Tel: 01763 249957* Contact Mary Demetriou

Iyengar Yoga Centre for Essex *Chelmsford. Tel: 01224 5421496* Contact Susan Long

London Borough of Barking & Dagenham Leisure Services *Ripple Road, Dagenham, Essex RM9. Tel: 020 8984 7694* If you cannot find a local yoga centre or a class from our listings, phone your local authority leisure services and see if they can help. Remember, yoga teachers often change venues or add classes to their programme, and local authorities often reorganise their activity programmes, adding and taking away classes on offer.

Outdoor Yoga in Essex *South East Essex Countryside. Tel: 01702 200386 yogacoach@hotmail.com* Weekly walks and yoga outdoors. The yoga sessions are held in various woodland and park settings – a lovely way to unwind, breathe some fresh air and yoga out the stress. Although British weather is often against it, outdoors is really the ideal place for yoga as the green environment helps you envision a bigger world than your ordinary concerns.

Satyananda Yoga Centre *Colchester. Tel: 01206 823383* Contact Swami Yogaprakash

School for Living Yoga *Loughton. Tel: 020 8502 4270* Contact Ernest Coates

Shanti Bhakti Sangha *Tel: 020 8549 2754* Contact Vera

ARDLEIGH Ardleigh Hall Leisure *Dedham Road, Ardleigh, Colchester, Essex CO7. Tel: 01206 230620* Ardleigh Hall Leisure has weekly yoga classes held during the day and in the evening. There are other exercise classes available too. Gym, squash, pool, and a spa area with steam room, sauna and jacuzzi. Bar.

BARKING Barking Abbey School Leisure Centre *Woodbridge Road, Barking, Essex IG11. Tel: 020 8270 6883 www.barking-dagenham.gov.uk* Lots of school use here at this big place but has recently had a refurbishment upgrade so the facilities are clean, pleasant and sometimes impressive.

BASILDON Club Kingswood *Clayhill Lane, Basildon, Essex SS16. Tel: 01268 522954* A members-only place so go along to see the facilities and watch one of the yoga classes. These are for both beginners and advanced students, held in the day and the evening. In addition to the yoga there are some 90 different classes per week going on. Private members-only fitness clubs are very competitive and often offer a jam-packed programme of activities to attract people. Could be too busy or could be really great fun. Look at some of the other classes so that you can get an idea of the standard of teaching and check that the instruction is not rushed. Facilities include gym, beauty salon and an aromatherapy room.

BASILDON Eversley Leisure Centre *2 Crest Avenue, Basildon, Essex SS13. Tel: 01268 583076* Weekly yoga. Adequate facilities with a fitness room, badminton courts and aerobic classes. Drinks machine on site.

BILLERICAY Agila Health & Fitness Centre *Unit 21 Bebington Close, Billericay, Essex CM12. Tel: 01277 630777* Wednesday afternoon and Sunday morning yoga sessions. Gym, martial arts classes, sauna, sunbeds. Crèche.

BRAINTREE Braintree Leisure Centre *Panfield Lane, Braintree, Essex CM7. Tel: 01376 552585* Weekly daytime yoga sessions. No evenings on offer at the moment. Aerobic classes and tennis but no pool or café.

BRENTWOOD Brentwood Centre *Doddinghurst Road, Pilgrims Hatch, Brentwood, Essex CM15. Tel: 01277 224386* The Brentwood Centre offers set courses in yoga that last a certain number of weeks. Two swimming pools, a gym, squash courts and a bar.

BURNHAM-ON-CROUCH Dengie Hundred Sports Centre *Millfields, Burnham-on-Crouch, Essex CM0. Tel: 01621 784633* Dengie Hundred Sports Centre offers thirteen-week yoga courses for beginners, intermediates and advance-level students. There are other classes like pilates. Beauty therapy room.

CHELMSFORD Danbury Sports & Social Centre *Danbury Fields, Main Road, Danbury, Chelmsford, Essex CM3. Tel: 01245 224515* Yoga, badminton and snooker. Bar.

CHELMSFORD Woodham Squash & Fitness Centre *Baron Road, South Woodham Ferrers, Chelmsford, Essex CM3. Tel: 01245 329882* Power Chi yoga plus regular yoga classes. Gym, squash courts, sauna and sunbeds. Bar.

CLACTON-ON-SEA Clacton Leisure Centre *Vista Road Recreation Ground, Clacton-on-Sea, Essex CO15. Tel: 01255 429647* Midweek evening yoga class. Swimming pool, tennis, badminton and loads of fitness classes and sessions. No bar but you can probably sneak into the one in the hockey club next door.

COLCHESTER Brightlingsea Sports Centre *Church Road, Brightlingsea, Colchester, Essex CO7. Tel: 01206 304946* Brightlingsea Sports Centre introduces you to yoga by holding a special induction course before you join up. This gives you a real chance to have a taster of yoga and gives the teacher time to assess your fitness and abilities. Gym, Step & Tone class, squash and badminton also on offer.

COLCHESTER LEISURE WORLD *Cowdray Avenue, Colchester, Essex CO1. Tel: 01206 282000* Daytime yoga sessions. Theme pool plus fitness training pool. Sauna, jacuzzi, gym, badminton and squash. Restaurant and bar.

COLCHESTER LEISURE WORLD Hamiltons Fitness Centre *Telford Way, Colchester Business Park, Colchester, Essex CO4. Tel: 01206 854319 hamiltonsfitness@aol.com www.hamiltonsfitness.co.uk* Evening yoga only. Gym. Aerobics studio. Sunbeds. Coffee bar.

FEERING Prested Hall *Prested Chase, Feering, Colchester, Essex CO5. Tel: 01376 572176 mail@prested.com www.prested.com* Regular yoga classes plus yoga for pregnancy (see next entry). Pilates course available. Twenty-metre pool, gym, tennis, real tennis, sauna and steam room. Brand new aerobics studio. Café.

FEERING Yoga for Pregnancy *Prested Hall, Prested Chase, Feering, Colchester, Essex CO5. Tel: 07739 559276 rnb@breathemail.net* Rachel Barrance gives these yoga classes. Yoga can help you in a gentle way to keep toned and fit during pregnancy when the extra weight and tiredness may make you feel like not going for a walk or doing exercises at home. In a group session there is mutual support – a great thing even at the best of times, never mind when you are feeling ratty and fed up. Contact Rachel for details and discuss with her the approach she takes. The calmer you are, the better it is for that growing baby. Rachel also teaches regular Hatha yoga classes – see Witham entry in this section.

HOCKLEY Clements Hall Leisure Centre *Clements Hall Way, Hawkwell, Hockley, Essex SS5. Tel: 01702 207777* A variety of yoga styles are on offer here, classes held mornings and evenings. Go along and discuss which style session might suit you best. Additional facilities include a gym, pool, squash, badminton and a health suite with sauna, steam room and three sunbeds. Bar and café.

HORNCHURCH Dragons Health Club *156 Abbs Cross Gardens, Hornchurch, Essex RM12. Tel: 01708 478077 www.dragons.co.uk* Drop-in evening classes only – yoga, pilates, boxercise, sunbeds, drinks at reception.

HORNCHURCH Hornchurch Sports Centre *Harrow Lodge Park, Hornchurch, Essex RM11. Tel: 01708 454729 www.hornchurchsportscentre.co.uk* Hornchurch Sports Centre yoga classes, offered in a six-week course block, are deservedly popular. There is usually a waiting list even though classes are held as often as four times a week. Dance and yoga studio. Pool, sauna and sunbeds. Badminton, martial arts, gym, personal training. Café and bar. Good activities for kids too. Crèche. A busy and friendly centre with evening classes. Excellent.

ILFORD Gymkhana *298 Green Lane, Ilford, Essex IG1. Tel: 020 85972 5552* A lively little place which tries very hard to please. Yoga and lots of other activities. Go see these people.

ILFORD Redbridge Sports & Leisure Centre *Forest Road, Ilford, Essex IG6. Tel: 020 8498 1000 www.rslonline.co.uk* Super centre. Everything from tennis to yoga.

LOUGHTON Body and Soul Health and Beauty Club *10 Torrington Drive, Debden, Loughton, Essex IG10. Tel: 020 8502 0175 info@body-soul.co.uk www.body-soul.co.uk* A yoga and pilates mixed system is offered here in twice-weekly classes. Other facilities include a gym, studio for classes, sauna, steam room, jacuzzi, sunbeds and toning tables. Body, soul and beauty – it hardly gets better.

LOUGHTON Methodist Church Hall *High Road, Loughton, Essex IG10. Tel: 020 8529 2931 geniebur@rosslyn0304. fsnet.co.uk* Twice-weekly yoga sessions.

MALDON Blackwater Leisure Centre *Park Drive, Maldon, Essex CM9. Tel: 01621 851898* Power Chi yoga! A grand mix of yoga and t'ai chi with day and evening sessions. The gym is for members only but other facilities include fitness classes, pool and café.

MALDON Park Drive Squash & Fitness Club *Park Drive, Maldon, Essex CM9. Tel: 01621 856036* Fitness yoga once a week. Facilities include squash, gym, sauna and jacuzzi. Coffee bar.

ROMFORD Health Club at City Limits *Collier Row Road, Collier Row, Romford, Essex RM5. Tel: 020 8924 2233 www.citylimits.co.uk* An out-of-town place with bars, restaurants, well-equipped fitness gym, pleasant studios. Regular yoga classes on offer.

ROMFORD Lady of America *3rd Floor, Liberty 2 Shopping Centre, Mercury Gardens, Romford, Essex RM1. Tel: 01708 754539* A women-only place to tone up, slim down and get some nutritional advice.

ROMFORD Romford YMCA *Rush Green Road, Rush Green, Romford, Essex RM1. Tel: 01708 766211 www.romfordymca.org* Wide-ranging programme. Busy place. Yoga and other classes. Café. Crèche.

ROMFORD Warren Sports Centre *Whalebone Lane North, Romford, Essex RM6. Tel: 020 8270 4488* Regular yoga class.

SAFFRON WALDEN Friends School *Saffron Walden, Essex*

CB1. Tel: 01223 890671 j_w.henrique@which.net Yoga with an emphasis on relaxation. Beginners and the experienced both welcomed.

SAFFRON WALDEN Lord Butler Fitness & Leisure Centre Peaslands Road, Saffron Walden, Essex CB11. Tel: 01799 522777 One daytime class here – but you can add on activities because they have a gym, squash, badminton and health spa with sauna and steam room. Recently refurbished.

SOUTH OCKENDON Belhus Park Leisure Centre Aveley, South Ockendon, Essex RM15. Tel: 01708 852248 Regular yoga during the day and in the evenings. Driving range, gym, swimming pool and sunbeds too.

SOUTHEND-ON-SEA Courtlands Club Wakering Road, Thorpe Bay, Southend-on-Sea, Essex SS1. Tel: 01702 586466 Yoga, t'ai chi, pilates and loads of other classes. Gym, pool, sauna, steam room and jacuzzi. Bar and café.

SOUTHEND-ON-SEA Fitness First (Southend) Ltd Thamesgate House, 33–41 Victoria Avenue, Southend-on-Sea, Essex SS2. Tel: 01702 390700 www.fitnessfirst.com yogacoach@hotmail.com Three big gyms here plus loads of classes including yoga for both beginners and intermediates. Daytime and evening classes. There is a sauna in the changing rooms which is exactly where one wants it. Free tea and coffee plus a lounge-about area.

SOUTHEND-ON-SEA Flights Leisure Aviation Way, Southend Airport, Southend-on-Sea, Essex SS2. Tel: 01702 540372 Get ready to refresh when you fly in! Three workout gyms, squash courts, aerobic classes, a sauna in the changing room, and you can enrol in either day or evening yoga classes.

SOUTHEND-ON-SEA Southend Leisure & Tennis Centre Garon Park, Eastern Avenue, Southend-on-Sea, Essex SS2. Tel: 01702 613000 Southendleisure@hotmail.com *www.leisure-centre.com/tennis.html* Weekly pay-as-you-go yoga class. Gym, sauna, steam room and sunbed. Bar serving food.

UPMINSTER Stan's Gym Health & Fitness Centre *Llantrisant Oaks, Aveley Road, Upminster, Essex RM14. Tel: 01708 227072* Open from noon till nine, plus Saturday and Sunday opening. The idea is this: you pay £35 per day to use the facilities, which include gym and cardio-fitness unit. All levels and ages welcome.

WESTCLIFF-ON-SEA Chase Sports & Fitness Centre *Prittlewell Chase, Westcliff-on-Sea, Essex SS0. Tel: 01702 433006 Southendleisure@hotmail.com* Yoga class every Monday plus a gym and sports hall. Bar.

WESTCLIFF-ON-SEA Westcliff Health Club *50 Valkyrie Road, Westcliff-on-Sea, Essex SS0. Tel: 01702 338046* Drop-in yoga classes during the day and in the evenings. Other classes such as aerobics on offer. Dance studio and three gyms. Sauna and steam room plus sunbeds. Bar. Café.

WITHAM Rachel Barrance Yoga *Witham, Essex CM8. Tel: 07739 559276 rnb@breathemail.net* A variety of Hatha yoga classes are on offer from this teacher, both daytime and evening. Suitable for all abilities and ages. Sessions are held around the Witham and Colchester areas.

WOODFORD GREEN Physicals Fitness Club *327 High Road, Woodford Green, Essex IG8. Tel: 020 8505 4914* This class combines forms and systems from yoga, t'ai chi and pilates. Aerobics also on offer plus a gym, sauna and three sunbeds. Small café.

HERTFORDSHIRE

GENERAL
Hertfordshire Yoga Workshop *St Albans. Tel: 01727 760067* Contact Kerstin Elliot

Kundalini Yoga & Meditation *St Albans. Tel: 01727 826183* Contact Valerie Crawford

Sivanada Yoga (Affiliated) *Parsonage Community Hall, Bishops Stortford, Hertfordshire. Tel: 01279 834670* Weekly yoga class with Sri Ramachandra (Nigel Kirby) for beginners, intermediates and advanced students.

Yoga Classes *Watford. Tel: 01923 856285* Contact Gillian Ellis

BARNET Queen Elizabeth's Sports Centre *Meadway, Barnet, Herts EN5. Tel: 020 8441 2933 www.barnet.gov.uk* An old, well-worn place up for renovation, but activities still go on, including very popular yoga classes.

BUNTINGFORD Benson Hall *Buntingford, Hertfordshire SG9. Tel: 01920 821288* General yoga class with teacher Jenny Harris, usually on a Monday.

BUSHEY Hartspring Leisure Centre *Park Avenue, Bushey, Watford, Hertfordshire WD2. Tel: 01923 233039* Daily yoga including Sundays – always a good day for yoga because it puts you in a good frame of mind for the week ahead.

GREAT HORMEAD Great Hormead Village Hall *Great Hormead, Hertfordshire SG9. Tel: 01920 821288* General yoga with Jenny Harris.

HARPENDEN Harpenden Sports Centre *Leyton Road, Harpenden, Hertfordshire AL5. Tel: 01582 767723* Pool, gym, sauna and steam room, squash, badminton and yoga classes each week. Café.

HATFIELD Birchwood Sports & Community Centre *Longmead, Hatfield, Hertfordshire AL10. Tel: 01707 270772* A yoga-based class which combines techniques and movements of yoga and pilates. Gym, badminton, netball, karate sessions and pilates.

HATFIELD Hatfield Leisure Centre *Travellers Lane, Hatfield, Hertfordshire AL10. Tel: 01707 268769* Regular yoga classes here during the week and on Sundays. In addition there are classes for the over 50s, which is a great idea. Facilities include badminton, squash, gym and other classes – see current programme.

HEMEL HEMPSTEAD Hatha Yoga with Cynthia Collisson *Hemel Hempstead, Hertfordshire HP1. Tel: 01442 391617* Contact teacher Cynthia Collisson on the above number to discover all about her Hatha yoga, relaxation and meditation classes.

HODDESDON John Warner Sports Centre *Stanstead Road, Hoddesdon, Hertfordshire EN11. Tel: 01992 445375* Lots of fitness classes here. Gym, pool, squash, and a sauna and steam room will soon be available. Café and bar.

LETCHWORTH The Health Studio *North Hertfordshire Leisure Centre, Baldock Road, Letchworth, Hertfordshire SG6. Tel: 01462 485344* Weekly yoga. Gym, 25-metre pool with slides, sauna, steam room, jacuzzi, café and bar all on offer

LETCHWORTH Iyengar Yoga *St Christopher's School, Letchworth, Hertfordshire SG6. Tel: 01462 679301* Iyengar yoga with John Lever. Contact him at the above number and discuss what's on offer.

LITTLE MUNDEN Little Munden School Hall *Dane End, Little Munden, Hertfordshire SG12. Tel: 01902 438416* Hazel.samurai@btopenworld.com Contact Hazel on the above number for information about this Tuesday evening class.

POTTERS BAR Furzefield Centre *Mutton Lane, Potters Bar, Hertfordshire EN6. Tel: 01707 850500* Two dance studios with weekly yoga classes. A 25-metre pool plus a huge gym facility, badminton, squash, health suite, sauna, jacuzzi and steam room completes the picture. This is the place to head for if you live locally.

POTTERS BAR Potters Fitness & Squash Club *Mount*

Grace Road, Potters Bar, Hertfordshire EN6. Tel: 01707 651086 Facilities include gym, squash court, sauna, steam room and sunbed. There is a café bar and a lounge area. The place has been in the process of refurbishment so drop by and see how it looks now.

POTTERS BAR Sportz Academy Limited *Darkes Lane, Potters Bar, Hertfordshire EN6. Tel: 01707 660777 www. sportzacademy.co.uk* Weekly yoga classes and good facilities – pool, gym, sauna, steam room, jacuzzi, café, bar and restaurant. A place to unwind with yoga and relaxation.

RICKMANSWORTH William Penn Leisure Centre *Shepherds Lane, Rickmansworth, Hertfordshire WD3. Tel: 01923 771050* Hatha yoga on offer along with a health suite, pool, squash courts, sauna, jacuzzi and a restaurant.

STEVENAGE David Lloyd Leisure *Stevenage Leisure Park, Kings Way, Stevenage, Hertfordshire SG1. Tel: 01438 847000 www.davidlloydleisure.co.uk* A members-only club. Yoga is regularly on the programme of activities. Gym, sauna, steam room, café and bar. Good standards.

STEVENAGE Odyssey Health & Rackets Club *Old Knebworth Lane, Stevenage, Hertfordshire SG2. Tel: 01438 313320* Studio for aerobics, pool, gym, squash court, tennis courts plus sauna and steam room. General yoga on the programme. Food available.

STEVENAGE R3 Leisure *North Road, Stevenage, Hertfordshire SG1. Tel: 01438 358071 enquiries@r3leisure. co.uk www.r3leisure.co.uk* On the current programme three types of yoga are on offer but call to find out exactly what's on when you want to enrol. There is a fully equipped gym plus relaxation facilities like sauna and steam room, sunbeds, beauty room and aromatherapy – plus a bar if all else fails to calm you down.

alth & Leisure Club *Manby Middlegate,*
...111. Tel: 01507 327293 Yoga is offered
. There is an aerobics studio, gym, pool,
acuzzi, toning tables and sunbed. A pub
distance but no in-house bar or café.

Station Sports & Leisure Centre
ethorpe, Lincolnshire LN12. Tel: 01507
ain this class? It's a mind and body work-
pilates and Alexander techniques. These
ll wonderful in themselves – but in com-
thing including the yoga tradition changes
go and watch a class to see if it's what
fun! Fitness suite. Sauna, steam room and
orts hall.

Earl of Scarborough Sports Centre
ss, Lincolnshire PE25. Tel: 01754 610352
and classes. Evening yoga classes only.
ennis, a climbing wall and trampolining.

British Wheel of Yoga *25 Jermyn*
Lincolnshire NG34. Tel: 01529 306851

aford Fitness & Leisure Station *Tamer*
e, Sleaford, Lincolnshire NG34. Tel: 01529
d traditional yoga. Lots of other classes on
ool, a gym, jacuzzi, sauna and steam room.
s available. Bar.

tle Sports Complex *Albion Street, Spalding,*
Tel: 01775 762178 Ten-week yoga courses.
es combination system. Gym. Aerobic and
sses too. Gym. Badminton, pool, sauna and
fé.

Vestside Health & Fitness Clubs *West*

ST ALBANS Batchwood Golf & Tennis Centre *Batchwood Hall, St Albans, Hertfordshire AL3. Tel: 01727 844250* Yoga four times a week. Tennis, squash, golf. Bar. An active, lively place.
ST ALBANS Bricket Wood Sports Centre *Smug Oak Lane, Bricket Wood, St Albans, Hertfordshire AL2. Tel: 01923 662224* Six-week yoga course. Pool, gym, sauna, sunbeds, tennis and squash. No café or bar but a vending machine.
ST ALBANS Friends Meeting House *7 Upper Lattimore Road, St Albans, Hertfordshire AL1. www.yoga123.co.uk* Hatha yoga for beginners and experienced students, which includes traditional shatkarma meditation and cleansing practices in the Satyananda tradition of the Bihar School of Yoga. Visit the website and learn more about these systems and details of the classes.
ST ALBANS Standon Village Hall *Hadham Road, Ware, Hertfordshire SG9. Tel: 01920 821288* Jenny Harris teaches a general yoga class here.
ST ALBANS Westminster Lodge Leisure Centre *Westminster Lodge, Holywell Hill, St Albans, Hertfordshire AL1. Tel: 01727 846031* More than 40 classes a week are held at this modern and popular centre. Gym, health suite, sauna, steam room and swimming pool. Café.
TRING Champneys *Wigginton, Tring, Hertfordshire HP23. Tel: 01442 291 000.* Luxury place. Yoga is only available for guests who are staying. Top-notch facilities include pool, gym, sauna, steam room, beauty treatments, restaurants, bar – everything you could want to relax, shape up and feel calm and beautiful. Treat yourself.
WALTHAM CROSS *Grundy Park Leisure Centre, Windmill Lane, Cheshunt, Waltham Cross, Hertfordshire EN8. Tel: 01992 623345* A well-placed leisure centre with yoga classes three times a week plus pool, gym, health suite, jacuzzi, sauna and

steam room. Café and bar.

WARE Ware Centre for Yoga Arts & Healing Sucklings Yard, Church Street, Ware, Hertfordshire SG12. Tel: 01920 466567 brigid@yogaware.fsnet.co.uk www.wareyoga.co.uk Wide variety of classes – yoga introduction, regular Astanga and Hatha yoga introduction.

WARE Wodson Park Sports & Recreation Centre Wadesmill Road, Ware, Hertfordshire SG12. Tel: 01920 487091 Yoga and other classes regularly on activities programme. Bar. Tidy and simple facility.

WATFORD Bill Everett Centre Leggatts Way, Watford, Hertfordshire WD2. Tel: 01923 441444 Weekly yoga classes. Other classes in the programme include aerobics and step workout. Pool. Bar.

WATFORD Charters Health Club Watford YMCA/Charter House, Charter Place, Watford, Hertfordshire WD1. Tel: 01923 353600 Pool, gym, sauna, steam room, café, bar and regular yoga classes. Straightforward but all you need.

WATFORD Sportz Academy Limited Gade House, 46 The Parade, Watford, Hertfordshire WD17. Tel: 01923 251800 www.sportzacademy.co.uk Yoga and other classes on offer. Pool, sauna and steam room.

WATFORD The Centre Gosforth Lane, Watford, Hertfordshire WD1. Tel: 020 8428 4954 Weekly classes for the yoga enthusiast. Limited facilities but there is a gym, fitness suite and café.

WELWYN GARDEN CITY Gosling Sports Park Stanborough Road, Welwyn Garden City, Hertfordshire AL8. Tel: 01707 331056 info@goslingsports.co.uk www.goslingsports. co.uk Yoga courses and classes on offer, as well as tennis, bowls, sauna and steam room. Café and bar.

GENER
Liz Chap
the Bourn
Leisure C
email and
be classes
Sally Wo
lineone.net
the area. C
BOURNE
Lincolnshire
combined. Fi
Gym. Bar. Ca
GAINSBOR
Gainsborough,
balance yoga,
Gym, pool, ma
steam room. B
GRANTHAM
Road, Grantham
week courses h
There are step
gym, pool, saun
GRIMSBY Gri
Grimsby, DN31.
teacher Pauline A
HOLBEACH Po
Spalding, Lincolnsh
positive-bodies.co.u
classes on offer. G

LOUTH Manby He
Louth, Lincolnshire LN
as a ten-week course
sauna, steam room,
is within staggering
MABLETHORPE
Station Road, Mabl
472129 How to exp
out combining yoga,
three systems are a
bination? Well, every
and evolves so bes
you want. Might be
sunbeds. Indoor sp
SKEGNESS The
Burgh Road, Skegne
Limited facilities
Badminton, short
SLEAFORD Th
Street, Sleaford,
office@bwy.org.uk
SLEAFORD Sle
Court, Church Lar
304770 Pilates an
offer too. Small p
Beauty treatment
SPALDING Cas
Lincolnshire PE11
A yoga and pilat
body balance cla
sunbeds. Bar. Ca
STAMFORD

Street, Stamford, Lincolnshire PE9. Tel: 01780 480651 info@
westsideclub.demon.co.uk   www.westsideclub.demon.co.uk
A weekly yoga class plus a great idea on Friday nights – a
yoga-based 'Friday Night Chill'. class. The club also has a gym,
beauty treatments, sauna and steam room. Check out the
website.

NORFOLK

GENERAL
Aylsham Meditation Group *Aylsham. Tel: 01263 732426*
Contact Cherry Cooke
Norfolk Iyengar Yoga Institute *c/o John & Ros Claxton The
Farmhouse, Booton, Near Peepham, Norfolk NR10.*
Norfolk Yoga Group *Tel: 01603 436659* Contact Bob Camp
BLICKLING Blickling Old School Hall *Blickling, Near
Aylsham, Norfolk NR11. Tel: 01603 465973 david@
david-farmer.com www.david-farmer.com* Yoga usually on a
Monday with teacher David Farmer. It's a friendly group, and
physical exercises, postures, breathing techniques and relax-
ation are included in the teaching. You will need to take your
own yoga mat.
**DOWNHAM MARKET Downham Market Sports
Centre** *Bexwell Road, Downham Market, Norfolk PE38. Tel:
01366 386868* Gym, pool, sunbeds, steam room and regular
yoga classes on offer. No café but there are vending machines.
GREAT YARMOUTH Broadland Sports Club *Main Road,
Fleggburgh, Great Yarmouth. Norfolk NR29. Tel: 01493 369651*
Lots of yoga classes plus fitness facilities, swimming, steam
room and tennis. Bar.
GREAT YARMOUTH Fitness 2000 *3 Steam Mill Lane, Great
Yarmouth, Norfolk NR31. Tel: 01493 442317* Now here is a
place that gives you real choice in yoga classes. There are

three types: Nice & Easy System Yoga Mixes, Pilates & Yoga, and T'ai Chi Yoga. Fully equipped gym, sunbeds and café. Spoiled for choice!

GREAT YARMOUTH Great Yarmouth Marina Leisure & Fitness Centre *Marine Parade, Great Yarmouth, Norfolk NR30. Tel: 01493 851521 www.thebiz.co.uk/yarmleis* A members-only gym so you have to join if you want to attend their regular classes. The Marina Centre has an interesting programme of classes based on yoga. These include body balance, stretch and relaxation classes. Sauna, pool, kiosk service for drinks.

GREAT YARMOUTH Norfolk Yoga Centre *Martham, Great Yarmouth, Norfolk NR29. Tel: 01493 748126 Maurice_yoga@web-sights.co.uk www.web-sights.co.uk/yoga*

HOLT Blakeney Sports Club *Langham Road, Blakeney, Holt. Norfolk NR25. Tel: 01263 741106* This telephone number gets you to the local council offices and they will give you details of where and when yoga is currently on offer.

KING'S LYNN Quay To Fitness *Matean House, Stonegate Street, King's Lynn, Norfork PE30. Tel: 01553 770062* Yoga classes are on offer in their new premises. New usually means good these days, so check out the facilities which include gym, sauna, sunbed, beauty treatments and massage. Coffee bar.

NORWICH Fitness Express *Barnham Broom Hotel, Honingham Road, Barnham Broom, Norwich, Norfolk NR9. Tel: 01603 759741* Yoga and other classes regularly held. Fully equipped gym, small pool with spa, squash, tennis, sports training. Bar. Restaurant.

NORWICH Lakenham Sports & Leisure Centre Ltd *Cricket Ground Road, Norwich, Norfolk NR1. Tel: 01603 477477* Yoga once a week. Gym, badminton and squash. Bar with some meals available.

NORWICH Long Stratton Leisure Centre *Swan Lane, Long Stratton, Norwich, Norfolk NR15. Tel: 01508 531444* Yoga once a week. Gym. Fitness suite. Some other classes on their programme as well. The bar is only open in the evenings.

NORWICH Nelson Leisure Club *Prince of Wales Road, Norwich, Norfolk NR1. Tel: 01603 214440* Yoga is on offer each week and there are nice facilities – a gym, pool, spa, sauna, steam room and café. If you become a member there are discounts usually on offer.

NORWICH No. 1 Gym Club *Ferodo House, 131–139 Queens Road, Norwich, Norfolk NR1. Tel: 01603 765600* Two yoga system classes offered here. One is a pure-form yoga class and the other yoga and pilates mixed. Facilities include a gym, sauna, steam room and sunbeds.

ROCKLAND ALL SAINTS Rockland Village Hall *Rockland All Saints, Norfolk NR17. Tel: 01953 860533* A mixed-ability class, based on Hatha yoga.

SHERINGHAM Splash Leisure Complex *Weybourne Road, Sheringham, Norfolk NR26. Tel: 01263 825675* The Splash Leisure Complex offers what they call Dynamic Yoga and Aerobic Yoga in a weekly class. Many teachers today in the West teach a combination of yoga movements, formulated into a system of exercise outside the traditional forms. This can be good although the yoga purist might think differently.

SWAFFHAM Swaffham Leisure Centre *Brandon Road, Swaffham, Norfolk PE37. Tel: 01760 724046* Aerobic yoga evening class each week. Gym, pool, badminton and sunbeds. Café.

THETFORD Breckland Leisure Centre & Water World *Croxton Road, Thetford, Norfolk IP24. Tel: 01842 753110* Three pools and loads of water fun here plus fitness centre, squash, a main sports hall and beginners classes in yoga.

WYMONDHAM Wymondham Leisure Centre *Norwich Road, Wymondham, Norfolk NR18. Tel: 01953 607171* Sunday morning yoga class. Pool, gym, aerobics, squash, sauna, steam room and sunbed. Café. Bar.

SUFFOLK

BECCLES Beccles Sports Centre *Ringsfield Road, Beccles, Suffolk NR34. Tel: 01502 712039* Weekly yoga class. Fitness room, martial arts classes, squash, tennis and badminton. Bar.

BRANDON Brandon Leisure Centre *Church Road, Brandon, Suffolk IP27. Tel: 01842 813748* A straightforward facility offering yoga and pilates classes plus gym, badminton and squash. Bar and function room.

BURY ST EDMUNDS Bury St Edmunds Leisure Centre *Beetons Way, Bury St Edmunds, Suffolk IP33. Tel: 01284 753496* Three pools and a number of courses on offer including yoga and fitness. Squash, badminton and café.

BURY ST EDMUNDS Moreton Hall Health Club *Moreton Hall, Mount Road, Bury St Edmunds, Suffolk IP32. Tel: 01284 704232* Power yoga classes. Squash, tennis, aerobic classes, two gyms, one mixed and one for women only. Small pool. Sauna and steam room. Bar.

BURY ST EDMUNDS Return to Top *Dome Leisure Centre, Bury Road, Mildenhall, Bury St Edmunds, Suffolk IP28. Tel: 01638 717737* Yoga courses during the day and four evenings a week. These are six-week courses but there is usually a waiting list to join. The current programme includes not just yoga but also pilates and t'ai chi. Fitness suite, badminton and squash.

FELIXSTOWE Felixstowe Leisure Centre *Undercliff Road West, Felixstowe, Suffolk IP11. Tel: 01394 670411* Yoga once a week, with gym, sauna and steam room. Café.

IPSWICH Clarice House *Bramford Road, Bramford, Ipswich, Suffolk IP8. Tel: 01473 463262 cdk@netcomuk.co.uk www.clarice.co.uk* Clarice House offers a ten-week yoga session course, suitable for all. They welcome you to just drop in and watch a class working out. There is a pool, gym, spa, sauna, steam room and hairdressing available, plus an aromatherapy room.

IPSWICH Group & Individual Hatha Yoga *Ipswich. Tel: 01473 405288* Contact Gillie Teacher who will travel to give a new class or individual instruction.

IPSWICH Hatha Yoga *Ipswich. Tel: 01473 219600* Contact Mike Linnet

IPSWICH Martlesham Leisure *Gloster Road, Martlesham Heath, Ipswich, Suffolk IP5. Tel: 01473 624707 david@ martleshamleisure.co.uk www.martleshamleisure.co.uk* General yoga class plus a Hatha yoga class which is more spiritually based and very soothing to mind and body. A pool and gym plus squash completes the exercise part of the facilities but there is a jacuzzi to help you unwind. Then you can use their bar and restaurant. A balanced set-up with popular yoga classes.

IPSWICH Return to Top *Chantry Sports Centre, Birkfield Drive, Ipswich, Suffolk IP2. Tel: 01473 602962* Weekly yoga class, fitness suite, badminton, football.

IPSWICH Vicky Noble Yoga *Ipswich. Tel: 01473 404863* Vicky Noble teaches Hatha yoga and offers a variety of classes: drop-in classes, Hatha yoga for prenatal and postnatal women, yoga for children and teenagers and a men-only class.

LEISTON Leiston Leisure Centre *Red House Lane, Leiston, Suffolk IP16. Tel: 01728 830364* A weekly class, Body Balancing, combines yoga and pilates. There is a 25-metre pool, a good gym, sauna, steam room and sunbed. No bar but there is a vending machine.

LOWESTOFT Waveney Sports Centre *Water Lane, Lowestoft, Suffolk NR32. Tel: 01502 569116* Weekly yoga classes, a pool, gym, sauna and steam room plus a nice bar and restaurant. Do the yoga bit, have some light food, and go home relaxed.

NEWMARKET Fizzique *Unit 5a Studlands Park Industrial Estate, Newmarket, Suffolk CB8. Tel: 01638 561228* Very popular place for yoga so book ahead for the sessions you want. A gym, sauna, toning tables and beauty treatment room are all on offer too. Small café.

NEWMARKET Newmarket Leisure Centre *Exning Road, Newmarket, Suffolk CB8. Tel: 01638 662726* A popular place so get in fast when they announce a new programme of classes because there is usually a waiting list. The classes are normally held on a weekly basis. There is squash, a gym and a small refreshment bar.

STOWMARKET Mid Suffolk Leisure Centre *Gainsborough Road, Stowmarket, Suffolk IP14. Tel: 01449 674980* Body balance course that combines yoga and pilates techniques. Three pools. Gym. Sauna and steam room. Bar and café. A good place to start yoga.

CENTRAL ENGLAND

WEST MIDLANDS

AMBLECOTE Misfits Gym *School Lane, Amblecote, West Midlands DY8. Tel: 01384 863590* Mixed-ability class usually held on a Wednesday.

BILSTON Life Foundation School for Therapeutics (UK) *Tel: 01902 409164* Contact Paulette Agnew

BIRMINGHAM Birmingham & District Institute of Iyengar Yoga *Birmingham. Tel: 0121 743 8143* Contact Jayne Orton

BIRMINGHAM Birmingham Sports Centre *Sherbourne Road, Balsall Heath, Birmingham, West Midlands B12. Tel: 0121 464 6060* Hatha yoga once a week. PulsePoint gym and cardio-vascular suite. Aerobic classes. Bar in evenings.

BIRMINGHAM Bruce's Gym Health & Fitness Centre *44 East Meadway, Birmingham, West Midlands B33. Tel: 0121 783 0050* A developing centre with yoga and other classes including circuit training. Boxercise, gym, saunas and sunbeds. Future plans include a café.

BIRMINGHAM Club Tropicana *366 Gravelly Lane, Birmingham, West Midlands B23. Tel: 0121 377 8081* Body balance, pilates and yoga plus other classes, all in a club with a gym, pool, sauna and steam room. Café and bar too.

BIRMINGHAM Courtneys Fitness For Life *21 Stephenson Street, Birmingham, West Midlands B2. Tel: 0121 643 1967* Lots of classes including yoga. A nice place to work out with a main gym, studio and steam room. No café but sandwiches and drinks available at reception.

BIRMINGHAM David Lloyd Club *Shady Lane, Birmingham, West Midlands B44. Tel: 0121 325 0700 www.davidlloyd*

leisure.co.uk The standard of this club is high and there are regular yoga classes, a gym, pool, beauty salon, massage, sauna and steam room. Restaurant.

BIRMINGHAM Great Barr Leisure Centre *Aldridge Road, Great Barr, Birmingham, West Midlands B44. Tel: 0121 464 0104* Simple and to the point – yoga class, gym, function room, badminton courts.

BIRMINGHAM Kingstanding Leisure Centre *Dulwich Road, Birmingham, West Midlands B44. Tel: 0121 464 7890* The yoga course is part of the adult education programme here so you must enrol. There are classes for both beginners and improvers. Pool, toning suite and gym. Café.

BIRMINGHAM LivingWell Health & Leisure *42-44 The Priory, Queensway, Birmingham, West Midlands B4. Tel: 0121 236 7789 www.livingwell.co.uk* Full range of classes, including Hatha yoga and Yoga Balance. The facilities include a pool, sauna, spa, steam room and a cardio-vascular fitness suite. Café and bar.

BIRMINGHAM Meridian Fitness Club *Aldridge Road, Great Barr, Birmingham, West Midlands B44. Tel: 0121 360 3939* Three yoga classes each week. Gym, sauna and sunbeds.

BIRMINGHAM The Moseley Dance Centre *572 Alcester Road, Moseley, Birmingham, West Midlands B13. Tel: 07941 547 251 j.s.hilton@talk21.com* Weekly yoga class, usually on a Tuesday. Take a mat.

BIRMINGHAM The Orange Room *424 Moseley Road, Balshall Heath, Birmingham, West Midlands B12. Tel: 07941 547251 j.s.hilton@talk21.com* Class held once a week on Thursdays. Bring your mat.

BIRMINGHAM Reviver *105 Piccadilly Arcade, Birmingham, West Midlands B2. Tel: 0121 643 3399* Plain and simple – yoga class, a gym, aerobics studio and sauna.

BIRMINGHAM Satyananda Yoga Centre *38 Gaddesby Road, Kings Heath, Birmingham, West Midlands B14. Tel: 0121 689 6269 little_sue@talk21.com*

BIRMINGHAM Satyananda Yoga Centre *Birmingham. Tel: 0121 444 5976* Contact Ann Fletcher

BIRMINGHAM Small Heath Leisure Centre *Muntz Street, Birmingham, West Midlands B10. Tel: 0121 464 6131* An active and fun place. A pool, two fitness rooms, dance room, netball, sports hall and aerobic and karate classes.

BIRMINGHAM Spirit Health & Fitness Club *The Post House, Chapel Lane, Great Barr, Birmingham, West Midlands B43. Tel: 0121 357 3223* Day and evening yoga classes plus loads of other classes including a holistic health course which combines pilates and yoga. The centre is part of a hotel complex so sauna, steam room and jacuzzi are also available. Café and bar.

BIRMINGHAM Stechford Cascades & Fitness Centre *Station Road, Stechford, Birmingham, West Midlands B33. Tel: 0121 464 5596* Two gyms, four pools and a general yoga class. Café.

BIRMINGHAM Stockland Green Leisure Centre *Slade Road, Birmingham, West Midlands B23. Tel: 0121 377 7880* Yoga once a week. Fitness room. No reason to linger.

BIRMINGHAM Viva Health & Leisure Clubs Ltd *3 Brunswick Arcade Brindleyplace, Birmingham, West Midlands B1. Tel: 0121 633 4645 info@viva.co.uk www.viva.co.uk* Great selection of yoga classes – Hatha, Yogalates and Iyengar. Beginners and intermediates welcomed. Gym, pool, sauna and steam room.

BRIERLEY HILL Helios Leisure Ltd *Thorns Road, Brierley Hill, West Midlands DY5. Tel: 01384 897700* Good place to start – yoga stretch and relax class, full gym, studio, pool, sauna, steam room, beauty suites and therapy rooms. Café and bar. We liked it.

DUDLEY Dudley Leisure Centre *Wellington Road, Dudley, West Midlands DY1. Tel: 01384 812815* Gym, pool, yoga once a week, badminton, squash. Neat and basic.

DUDLEY Figures *Unit 4 Holborn Centre, High Holborn, Dudley, West Midlands DY3. Tel: 01902 666069* There is a general yoga class for all levels of ability. Lots of other classes plus a gym, sauna and toning tables. An OK place.

DUDLEY Hillcrest Leisure Centre *Simms Lane, Dudley, West Midlands DY2. Tel: 01384 816503* This leisure centre runs the yoga classes as part of its adult education programme. Fitness room and sports hall.

HALESOWEN Universal Fitness *1st Floor Regent House, Queensway, Halesowen, West Midlands B63. Tel: 0121 550 5400* Sunday yoga. Gym, aerobics and sauna.

KINGSWINFORD Crestwood School *Bromley Lane, Kingswinford, West Midlands DY6. Tel: 01384 863590* Intermediates on a Thursday.

KINGSWINFORD Fortnocks Ultimate Health & Fitness Centre *8a Stallings Lane, Kingswinford, West Midlands DY6. Tel: 01384 401408* Body balance class. Gym, sauna, sunbeds, beauty therapist on site.

KINGSWINFORD Misfits Gym *High Street, Kingswinford, West Midlands DY6. Tel: 01384 863590* Mixed-ability class on a Friday.

LEAMINGTON SPA National Spiritualist Church *Holly Street, Leamington Spa, West Midlands CV37. Tel: 01789 204753 sandibottone@stannifer.co.uk* Monday yoga.

SHIRLEY Shirley Community Association Yoga Class *Shirley. Tel: 0121 744 6330* Contact Evelyn Hewett

SMETHWICK Fitness First (Birmingham) Ltd *477–489*

Hagley Road, Smethwick, West Midlands B66. Tel: 0121 434 3737 www.fitnessfirst.com If you're talking facilities and access, this place takes the cake! You can go around the world with your membership at Fitness First – you can use 315 fitness places worldwide. Why not yoga around the planet? This branch has a huge number of classes to choose from including yoga twice a week and pilates. There are unisex and women-only gyms. With a relaxation area plus sauna, steam room and aromatherapy, you need never go long without a destressing session. To top it all off, they give you free tea and coffee. You can even order breakfast and read the free newspapers.

SOLIHULL Club Motivation *61 Homer Road, Solihull, West Midlands B91. Tel: 0121 709 0274* Yoga for all levels plus two gyms, a pool, sauna, steam room, spa, beauty treatments and a café and bar.

SOLIHULL David Lloyd Club *Highlands Road, Shirley, Solihull, West Midlands B90. Tel: 0121 712 1600 www.david lloydleisure.co.uk* A load of facilities and classes. The yoga classes include general yoga as well as Ashtanga. There is a good gym, a pool, sauna, steam room, spa and jacuzzi, as well as beauty treatments if you want them. Restaurant and bar. One of the best places in the area.

SOLIHULL David Lloyd Club *247 Cranmore Boulevard, Shirley, Solihull, West Midlands B90. Tel: 0121 733 5300 www.davidlloydleisure.co.uk* Big, popular and busy! Seven tennis courts, squash, gym, beauty and health rooms, sauna, steam and jacuzzi. For yoga you can choose Hatha or Ashtanga. Open weekends so you can look round – go on, do it!

SOLIHULL Shirley Institute *Church Road, Shirley, Solihull, West Midlands B90. Tel: 01564 777969 michelleallen@ knowle176.freeserve.co.uk* All-year-round yoga on a Tuesday morning – take a mat and small blanket.

SOLIHULL Streetsbrook Infant School *Ralph Road, Shirley, Solihull, West Midlands B90. Tel: 01564 777969 michelleallen@knowle176.freeserve* Yoga class in the evenings during term-time. Take a mat and small blanket.

SOLIHULL United Reformed Church *Faulkner Road, Off Castle Lane, Solihull, West Midlands B92. Tel: 01564 777969 michelleallen@knowle176.freeserve* Popular classes here, held on Thursday mornings and Wednesday evenings (except August). Spaces can be limited so call first. Take a mat and blanket.

SOLIHULL Viva Health & Leisure Clubs Ltd *Saintbury Drive, Solihull, West Midlands B91. Tel: 0121 705 2444 info@viva.co.uk www.viva.co.uk* Lots of different classes for all levels. A health club with all the trimmings. Gym, sauna and steam room, spa, jacuzzi, beauty rooms and more. Café too. Enjoy.

STOURBRIDGE Crystal Leisure Centre *Health & Fitness Suite, Bell Street, Stourbridge, West Midlands DY8. Tel: 01384 812912* Yoga every day and evening – you just drop in. Two pools, a gym, aerobic classes, sauna, steam room and jacuzzi. Or you can laze back with a drink from the bar and watch people swimming in the pool. Great stuff.

STOURBRIDGE Fitness Academy *Lower High Street, Stourbridge, West Midlands DY8. Tel: 01384 443401* A health and healing orientated place with a homeopathic practitioner on the premises for consultations. Yoga classes are held for all levels. A gym, fitness studio, beauty suite, sauna and spa complete the picture. Crèche.

SUTTON COLDFIELD Moor Hall Health & Leisure Club *Moor Hall Hotel, Moor Hall Drive, Sutton Coldfield, West Midlands B75. Tel: 0121 308 8030* Yoga, pilates and body balance three times a week. Pool, sauna, steam room, beauty treatments and bar.

SUTTON COLDFIELD Wyndley Leisure Centre *Clifton Road, Sutton Coldfield, West Midlands B73. Tel: 0121 464 7742* Three forms of yoga are usually on offer – general, Hatha and Ashtanga. There's also Yogasize, which is a bit of a mystery to us even now. If you find out exactly what it is, let us know.

WALSALL One On One Fitness Centre *Pleck Road, Walsall Manor Hospital, Walsall, West Midlands WS2. Tel: 01922 624663* A main gym and a smaller one are at the heart of this place, but yoga classes are on offer. Good dance studio. Sauna, steam room and jacuzzi.

WALSALL Reviver *9–10a The Bridge, Walsall, West Midlands WS1. Tel: 01922 637224* A pleasant facility offering all the basics you need – a general-level class of yoga, a gym, aerobics studio, sauna and coffee lounge.

WILLENHALL Willenhall Leisure Centre *Bath Street, Willenhall, West Midlands WV13. Tel: 01902 368663* General yoga classes, held in the daytime and evenings. Gym, pool, badminton and other classes. Try the water-aerobics class for a change of exercise style.

WOLVERHAMPTON Codsall Leisure Centre *Elliotts Lane, Codsall, Wolverhampton, West Midlands WV8. Tel: 01902 844032* Register before each term if you want to join the yoga class here because they run for a certain length of time. Facilities include a 25-metre pool, sports hall, badminton, two squash courts, fitness room, tennis courts and sunbeds. Bar. One of the best places in the area.

WOLVERHAMPTON Graiseley Recreation Centre *Pool Street, Wolverhampton, West Midlands WV2. Tel: 01902 552355* A basic centre with yoga classes twice a week, two gyms and an aerobics area.

WOLVERHAMPTON The Parkdale Yoga Centre *10 Parkdale West, Wolverhampton WV1. Tel: 01902 424048 info@heartyoga.org.uk www.heartyoga.og.uk* Located in the southern part of Wolverhampton, the Parkdale Yoga Centre is run by a small urban commune which focuses on yoga practice and teaching, organic growing and holistic living. There are a host of yoga classes held here so call to find out what is available and to discuss your level and requirements. Beginners yoga and intermediate and advanced classes available. There are summer yoga retreats and weekend yoga retreats on offer plus a special beginners weekend yoga retreat.

WOLVERHAMPTON Reviver *20 Snow Hill, Wolverhampton, West Midlands WV2. Tel: 01902 772356* Yoga classes for all levels plus gym, exercise classes, sauna and coffee area.

WOLVERHAMPTON Wolverhampton Lawn Tennis and Squash Club *Neville Lodge, Newbridge Crescent, Tettenhall, Wolverhampton, West Midlands WV6. Tel: 01902 752231* Yoga and pilates classes. Dance studio to really get you moving. Two saunas and a restaurant and bar. Nice place.

WOLVERHAMPTON Wombourne Leisure Centre *Ounsdale Road, Wombourne, Wolverhampton, West Midlands WV5. Tel: 01902 898202* Full exercise programme including yoga, pilates and line dancing. Gym and pool too. You get a warm welcome here.

BUCKINGHAMSHIRE

GENERAL

Buckinghamshire Iyengar Yoga *Tel: 01753 882112 moni@alt128.co.uk* Monika Steiner Celebi teaches Iyengar yoga and antenatal classes in and around Buckinghamshire.

South Bucks Yoga with Manoj *manojn@vossnet.co.uk* Manoj teaches integral yoga in south Buckinghamshire in small groups.

AYLESBURY Belmore Centre *Risborough Road, Stoke Mandeville, Aylesbury, Buckinghamshire HP22. Tel: 01296 612361* Health and beauty centre plus various therapies and treatments including osteopathy, acupuncture and hypnotherapies. Pilates and yoga on offer but you must enrol first.

AYLESBURY Guttmann Sports & Leisure Centre *Stoke Mandeville Sports Stadium, Guttmann Road, Aylesbury, Buckinghamshire HP21. Tel: 01296 484848* A general-level yoga workshop is on offer with classes in the evening as well. Gym, pool, sports hall, running track, sauna and sunbed. Café and bar.

AYLESBURY Spirit Health & Fitness Club *Aston Clinton Road, Weston Turville, Aylesbury, Buckinghamshire HP22. Tel: 01296 399220* Spirit holds three yoga classes a week aimed at all levels. One of them should be just right for you. There is a gym, pool, sauna, steam room and jacuzzi. Beauty therapy available too. Nice.

BEACONSFIELD Beacon Centre *Holtspur Way, Beaconsfield, Buckinghamshire HP9. Tel: 01494 677764* Loads of classes here from yoga to pilates. Gym, sports hall, badminton, sunbed. Also a theatre showing local productions!

BLETCHLEY Bletchley Leisure Centre *Princes Way, Bletchley, Milton Keynes, Buckinghamshire MK2. Tel: 01908 377251* Good place. All levels of yoga class every week. Gym, pool, sauna, jacuzzi, steam room. Fitness classes plus badminton and squash. Visiting therapists and teachers run courses on body mobility and massage. Café and bar.

BUCKINGHAM Swan Pool & Leisure Centre *London Road, Buckingham, Buckinghamshire MK18. Tel: 01280 817500*

Practical place. Yoga sessions once a week. Two pools, gym, dance classes, squash, sauna and sunbeds.

CHALFONT ST PETER Chalfont Leisure Centre *Nicol Road, Chalfont St Peter, Gerrards Cross, Buckinghamshire SL9. Tel: 01494 788977* Beginners and intermediate yoga plus pilates. A very good centre with a 25-metre pool, swimming lessons, Aquatone, sports hall, football, badminton, gymnastics, judo, karate classes, two gyms. Sauna, steam room and spa too. This is an all-singing, all-dancing place. One of the best centres.

CHESHAM Topnotch Health Ltd *Amersham Road, Chesham, Buckinghamshire HP5. Tel: 01494 774100* Lots going on at this pleasant and professionally run place. Various yoga classes including Hatha and Yogalates. Two gyms, dance studio, sauna, steam room, beautician, physiotherapist, crèche, café and bar.

HIGH WYCOMBE Bodyshack Fitness Centre *4b Desborough Industrial Park, Desborough Park Road, High Wycombe, Buckinghamshire HP12. Tel: 01494 442235* Yoga classes open to everyone. Fitness studio, fully equipped gym, sauna and sunbeds.

HIGH WYCOMBE Great Marlow School *Adult Education Section, Kingshill Road, High Wycombe, Buckinghamshire HP13. Tel: 01494 473795 www.adultedbucks.org.uk* Midweek yoga class for mixed abilities. Take a mat and small blanket.

IVER Evreham Centre *Swallow Street, Iver, Buckinghamshire SL0. Tel: 01753 672610 tim.naylor@talk21.com* Weekly yoga class for beginners.

MILTON KEYNES David Lloyd Leisure *Livingstone Drive, Newlands, Milton Keynes, Buckinghamshire MK15. Tel: 01908 207900 www.davidlloydleisure.co.uk* Expensive but you get what you pay for. Three gyms, 86 classes a week including yoga, pools, tennis, sauna, steam room, beauty therapy and massage. Coffee shop, bar and restaurant. A swanky place.

MILTON KEYNES Dragons Health Club *Brickhill Street, Willen Lake, Milton Keynes, Buckinghamshire MK15. Tel: 01908 295699 www.dragons.co.uk* Good selection of classes in a modern facility.

MILTON KEYNES Esporta Health & Fitness Club *Xscape Building, 602 Marlborough Gate, Milton Keynes, Buckinghamshire MK9. Tel: 01908 298800 www.esporta.com* Right up to the mark and among the best places. So central you'll find it hard not to go on to other activities after your yoga class.

MILTON KEYNES Flex Appeal Fitness Centre & Aerobic Studio *Glyn Square, Wolverton, Milton Keynes, Buckinghamshire MK12. Tel: 01908 313412* Yoga Balance – a class for fitness and balance that includes a number of yoga movements. Go and have a look and see if it's for you. Limited facility with a weight-training gym and sauna.

MILTON KEYNES Harpers Fitness *Bletchley Leisure Centre, Princes Way, Bletchley, Milton Keynes, Buckinghamshire MK2. Tel: 01908 377251 www.harpersfitness.co.uk* An outstanding leisure centre with classes, pools, courts, crèche and snooker.

MILTON KEYNES LivingWell Health Club *477–488 Avebury Boulevard, Milton Keynes, Buckinghamshire MK9. Tel: 01908 668286 www.livingwell.co.uk* All the facilities you would expect. Gym, pool, sauna, steam room, spa, hair and beauty salons and massages. Beginners and intermediate yoga classes plus a general-ability class.

MILTON KEYNES Lorraine Blake's Fitness Club *Chanity & Guildhall, Watling Street, Fenny Stratford, Bletchley, Milton Keynes, Buckinghamshire MK2. Tel: 01908 644444* A friendly and well-respected club. A general yoga class is on offer, suitable for all levels of ability. There are two gyms, one mixed and one for women only. Other classes besides yoga, including pilates.

MILTON KEYNES Shenley Leisure Centre *Burchard Crescent, Shenley Church End, Milton Keynes, Buckinghamshire MK5. Tel: 01908 5024881 www.slc-mk.org.uk* Easy on the wallet, a no-frills place with most of the facilities you might want to go along with your regular yoga class. Weekly yoga class suitable for most levels. Fitness room, various aerobic classes and sunbed. Bar.

MILTON KEYNES Woughton Leisure Trust *Woughton Centre, Rainbow Drive, Leadenhall, Milton Keynes. Buckinghamshire MK6 Tel: 01908 660392* A well-equipped place with pool, gym, tennis courts and sunbeds. Group yoga classes of mixed ability, but go along and see if it suits. Big aerobics programme of classes and courses. Bar in the evenings.

OLNEY Susan Hill Yoga *The Olney Centre, High Street, Olney, Buckinghamshire MK46. Tel: 01525 634873 sue_yoga@hotmail.com www.sueyoga.freeservers.com* Both beginners and intermediates catered for. Iyengar yoga. Exercises are graded to ensure safety.

PRESTWOOD Prestwood Methodist Church Hall *High Street, Prestwood, Buckinghamshire HP16. Tel: 01494 863088* Yoga classes twice a week.

PRINCES RISBOROUGH Risborough Springs Swim & Fitness Centre *Wades Park, Stratton Road, Princes Risborough, Buckinghamshire HP27. Tel: 01844 274200* General yoga plus some other classes. Pool and gym. Basic place.

SEER GREEN Hatha Yoga Seer Green *Princess Marina Centre, Chalfont Road, Seer Green, Buckinghamshire HP9.*

Tel: 01494 678140 Weekly class for beginners to intermediates.
WENDOVER St Anne's Hall *Aylesbury Road, Wendover, Buckinghamshire HP22. Tel: 01296 628788* Lots of yoga classes held in this busy but pretty village, mornings and evenings.

DERBYSHIRE

ALFRETON St Thomas's Parish Hall *Somercotes, Near Alfreton, Derbyshire DE5. Tel: 01773 528264 LS@sole9. fsnet.co.uk www.soleinsights.co.uk* Hatha yoga with Lisa.
BELPER The Fit Pit *East Mill, Bridge Foot, Belper, Derbyshire DE56. Tel: 01773 821676 www.thefitpit.com* Studio for aerobics and yoga classes, which are run three times a week. Fairly basic place that concentrates on fitness rather than relaxation facilities.
CHESTERFIELD Derbyshire Yoga Teachers' Association *Chesterfield. Tel: 01773 822033* Contact Russell Brown
CHESTERFIELD Friends Meeting House *Brockwell Lane, Chesterfield, Derbyshire S41. Tel: 07946 389505* General Hatha yoga classes several times a week.
CHESTERFIELD Middlecroft Leisure Centre *Middlecroft Road South, Chesterfield, Derbyshire S43. Tel: 01246 345666 lee.allcock@chesterfieldbc.gov.uk* Excellent centre with yoga and other classes plus pool, gym, badminton, squash, table tennis, steam room, sunbeds. Crèche. Café bar.
CHESTERFIELD Queen's Park Sports Centre *Boythorpe Road, Chesterfield, Derbyshire S40. Tel: 01246 345555 qpsc@chesterfieldbc.gov.uk www.chesterfieldboroughcouncil. co.uk* Well-run local authority centre with yoga and other classes. Pool, gym, squash, badminton, sauna and steam room plus crèche and café.
DERBY David Lloyd Racquet & Fitness Club *Pride Park, Riverside Road, Derby, Derbyshire DE24. Tel: 0990 616263*

www.davidlloydleisure.co.uk David Lloyd clubs often have yoga classes, so check the programmes from time to time to see what's been added.

DERBY Fitness First (Derby) Ltd *St Thomas House, Mansfield Road, Derby, Derbyshire DE1. Tel: 01332 297444 www.fitnessfirst.com* Well-equipped club with yoga classes, gym, sauna, steam room, spa, therapy room, beauty salon, DVD/video library and a juice bar. Nice one!

DERBY Lady in Leisure *St James Street, Derby, Derbyshire DE1. Tel: 01332 200446 www.revivahouseclubs.co.uk* You may be a lady of leisure but you will be a busy one here. The facilities are good with a gym, aerobics classes, t'ai chi, toning tables, hair and beauty salon and weekly yoga.

DERBY Moorways Leisure Complex *Moor Lane, Allenton, Derby, Derbyshire DE24. Tel: 01332 363686 www.derbysports.co.uk* Another good centre. Three classes of yoga a week plus pool, gym, squash, badminton, crèche and café.

DERBY Virgin Active *Derbyshire Cricket Club, Nottingham Road, Derby, Derbyshire DE21. Tel: 01332 287900 john@virgin-active.co.uk www.virginactive.com/active* Yoga classses plus pool, spa, jacuzzi, pilates classes and a crèche.

FINDFERN Findfern Village Hall *Findfern, Derbyshire DE 65. Tel: 01283 703940 cwhitby@parker.com*

GLOSSOP Glossop Leisure Centre *High Street East, Glossop, Derbyshire SK13. Tel: 01457 863223 www.glossop.com* Gym, sports hall, squash, yoga classes. Crèche. Bar.

ILKESTON Albion Leisure Centre *East Street, Ilkeston, Derbyshire DE7. Tel: 0115 944 0200* General yoga class but so popular that you must book in advance and there is usually a waiting list to join. The facility has a gym, badminton and a family sports centre. Café and bar. Great place for all.

MARPLE Marple Senior Citizens Hall *Marple, Derbyshire SK22. Tel: 0161 336 5261 (Ask for Ted) yoga4nel@onetel.net.uk*
MATLOCK Sherwood Hall Leisure Centre *Lime Tree Road, Matlock, Derbyshire DE4. Tel: 01629 56111* leisure@sherwoodhallddc.fsnet.co.uk Yoga class in a basic centre.

GLOUCESTERSHIRE

GENERAL Gloucestershire Integral Yoga *Redmarley. Tel: 01531 820354* Contact Brenda Judge
BROCKWORTH Club Moativation *Cheltenham & Gloucester Moat House, Shurdington Road, Brockworth, Gloucester, Gloucestershire GL3. Tel: 01452 512703* A hotel leisure centre – just what the doctor ordered when you're travelling but locals can take out membership and get discounts too. There are yoga classes for beginners and intermediates plus Power yoga. Dance studio, gym, sauna, steam room and pool. Bar and restaurant.
CHELTENHAM Peak Fitness Cheltenham *Sandford Parks Lido, Keynsham Road, Cheltenham, Gloucestershire GL53. Tel: 01242 257700 cheltenham@peak-fitness.co.uk www.peak-fitness.co.uk* Four yoga classes along with others such as t'ai chi. Gym and sports massage. This is a small club but very lively and sociable.
CIRENCESTER Le Spa at Stratton Place *Gloucester Road, Cirencester, Gloucestershire GL7. Tel: 01285 653840 mail@lespainternational.co.uk www.lespainternational.co.uk* Warm welcome and a pleasant place to be. General yoga class twice a week. Gym, spa, sauna, steam room, jacuzzi, beauty treatments and massage. Café and bar.
CIRENCESTER Viniyoga Cotswolds *Cirencester. Tel: 01285 750293* Contact Mary Harris
COLEFORD Five Acres Leisure Centre *Berry Hill, Coleford,*

Gloucestershire GL16. Tel: 01594 835388 Yoga once a week, pool, squash, badminton. Drinks machine. No-frills place.

COLEFORD Forest of Dean Gymnastics & Fitness Centre *Five Acres, Coleford, Gloucestershire GL16. Tel: 01594 833393* A basic fitness centre with yoga and some other classes plus gym.

DURSLEY Courtyard Health & Fitness Ltd *12 Parsonage Street, Dursley, Gloucestershire GL11. Tel: 01453 546454* Yoga classes three times a week plus other classes. Exercise studio, gym, physiotherapy clinic. No pool in the facility but one just over the road.

GLOUCESTER Warehouse Climbing Centre & Health Club *Parliament Street, Gloucester, Gloucestershire GL1. Tel: 01452 302351 www.the-warehouse.co.uk* All-levels yoga class once a week plus gym, weights area, steam room and jacuzzi. Bar.

KEMBLE Forge House Centre *Kemble. Tel: 01285 770635* Contact Michael Lawlor

LYDNEY Lydney Whitecross Leisure Centre *Church Road, Lydney, Gloucestershire GL15. Tel: 01594 842383* Compared to some counties, Gloucestershire has a great choice of good clubs and leisure centres where you can find yoga in pleasant surroundings. Here is another one. Lydney holds yoga and yoga plus pilates classes. There is also a body balance class. You book for a course lasting a set number of weeks. Pool, fitness suite, gym, sports hall, badminton and squash courts complete the picture.

QUEDGELEY Peak Fitness *35 Olympus Park, Quedgeley, Gloucestershire GL2. Tel: 01452 721888 gloucester@peak-fitness.co.uk www.peak-fitness.co.uk* Yoga once a week. Gym, studio, sauna and steam room. Jacuzzi. That's it.

STROUD Chestnut House Ladies Health & Beauty Spa

Chestnut House, Bowbridge, Stroud, Gloucestershire GL5. Tel: 01453 751500 Chestnut House has loads of classes including pilates and yoga. Nice gym, pool, jacuzzi, sauna and steam room, toning table and aqua aerobics. Bistro. Pleasant, professional place.

STROUD Hawkwood College *Painswick Old Road, Stroud, Gloucester GL6. Tel: 01453 759034 hawkwoodcollege@cs.com* Hawkwood provides a beautiful setting for a yoga or other retreat, adult education courses and conferences. The facilities are centred around a nineteenth-century manor house with fields and woodlands. Open all year. Garden, library, guest lounge, TV. Everyone eats together. Traditional wholefood. Vegetarians and special diets catered for.

STROUD Le Spa at Chestnut House *Bowbridge, Stroud, Gloucestershire GL5. Tel: 01453 751500 mail@lespainternational.co.uk www.lespainternational.co.uk* Full range of classes here including yoga. Facilities include a pool, gym, toning tables, beauty therapy room, sauna, steam room and jacuzzi. Bistro. Good place.

HEREFORDSHIRE

BROMYARD Bromyard Leisure Centre *Cruxhall Street, Bromyard, Herefordshire HR7. Tel: 01885 482195* Yoga classes are offered as an eight-week course. Fitness suite, function suite and bar.

HEREFORD Hereford Leisure Centre *Holmer Road, Hereford HR4. Tel: 01432 278178* Community sports centre plus yoga classes during the week.

LEDBURY Canon Frome Court *Ledbury, Herefordshire HR8. Tel: 01531 670540 information@canonfromecourt.org.uk www.canonfromecourt.org.uk* A community of some 30 adults established in the late 1970s. It continues to be a thriving place with a number of activities including a farm, workshops for metal, wood and basket making and a furniture store. Wholefoods and chocolate are on sale too. There is a huge hall for occasional courses, which include yoga. A number of outbuildings, and goats, sheep, chickens, geese, bees and children abound. Nice place.

LEOMINSTER Bridge Street Park Sports Centre *Leominster, Herefordshire HR6. Tel: 01568 611172* Contact for yoga class: 01544 387960.

LEICESTERSHIRE

GENERAL

Leicestershire Area Yoga *Tel: 01162 706399* Teacher Anne-Marie Newland holds classes in various parts of the Leicester area.

Leicestershire Yoga Circle *Tel: 01162 793594* Contact Brenda Kirby

ASHBY-DE-LA-ZOUCH Angels *Holywell Mill, Burton Road, Ashby-de-la-Zouch, Leicestershire LE65. Tel: 01530 412050* Power Chi yoga, private gym for women only. Sauna, spa, steam room and jacuzzi. Toning tables and beauty treatment rooms complete this pleasant place. Lounge for tea or coffee.

ASHBY-DE-LA-ZOUCH Hood Park Leisure Centre *North Street, Ashby-de-la-Zouch, Leicestershire LE65. Tel: 01530 412181* Regular yoga classes plus a gym, indoor and outdoor pools, dance studio and sports hall. Bar in the evenings. Excellent centre with all you need for relaxation of mind and body.

ASHBY-DE-LA-ZOUCH Springs Health Farm *Arlic Farm, Gallows Lane, Packington, Ashby-de-la-Zouch, Leicestershire LE65. Tel: 01530 273873 enquiries@henlowgrange.co.uk www.healthfarms.co.uk* Springs Health Farm has all you need and more. For the yoga classes there are two qualified instructors, and they include Hatha yoga and Kundalini yoga. Gym, pool, sauna, steam room and jacuzzi. More than 80 therapists serve Springs Health farm so many different healing and relaxing treatments are available. There are two different restaurants plus a spa café. Dead posh!

COALVILLE Hermitage Leisure Centre *Silver Street, Whitwick, Coalville, Leicestershire LE67. Tel: 01530 811215* Yoga is taken seriously here. There are yoga classes for all levels including Yoga Strength, which is for the more advanced practitioner. High-tech gym, pool, squash, badminton, health suite, sauna, steam room and jacuzzi complete this excellently equipped centre. Café and bar in the evenings.

HINCKLEY Fields Health & Fitness Club *Wheatfield Way, Hinckley, Leicestershire LE10. Tel: 01455 233337* A general yoga class plus gym, mixed sauna and beauty treatment salon. Coffee lounge. Nice!

HINCKLEY Hinckley Leisure Centre *Coventry Road, Hinckley, Leicestershire LE10. Tel: 01455 610011* Body balance class, which is a mix of yoga and pilates. Facilities include a gym, pool, squash and badminton. Café and bar. All you need under one roof.

LEICESTER Aylestone Leisure Centre *2 Knighton Lane East, Leicester, Leicestershire LE2. Tel: 0116 233 3040* General yoga class on offer and no need to book – just drop in. There is a pool, aqua aerobics and aerobics. Café.

LEICESTER David Lloyd Leisure *Meridian Leisure Park, Lubbesthorpe Way, Braunstone, Leicester, Leicestershire LE3. Tel: 0116 282 8800 www.davidlloydleisure.co.uk* Lots of good facilities here. A huge fully equipped gym, sauna, steam room and spa. An aerobics studio and more than 40 classes per week including yoga and martial arts. A number of social events as well. Pool and café. Altogether one of the best places.

LEICESTER Lady In Leisure *24a Belgrave Gate, Leicester, Leicestershire LE1. Tel: 0116 251 5166* General yoga classes and other classes like pilates. Gym. Sauna. Coffee lounge.

LEICESTER Life Unlimited Health & Fitness Club *40 High Street, Earl Shilton, Leicester, Leicestershire LE9. Tel: 01455 843498* Yoga plus a class of yoga and pilates mix. Aerobics class also on the programme. Friendly and helpful place. Gym, sauna and steam room.

LEICESTER L'Image *Leisure Centre, Mill Lane, Enderby, Leicester, Leicestershire LE9. Tel: 0116 286 6881* Body balance, a mix of yoga and pilates, is on offer at L'Image. There is a good 25-metre pool, big gym, sauna, sunbeds, café and a bar in the evenings. We liked it.

LEICESTER Southfields Drive Sports Centre *Southfields Drive, Leicester, Leicestershire LE2. Tel: 0116 283 9047* Yoga class once a week. Other classes on the programme too. Gym and a small coffee bar. Simple but OK place.

LOUGHBOROUGH Isospa *Charnwood Leisure Centre, Browns Lane, Loughborough, Leicestershire LE11. Tel: 01509 230698* Ten-week yoga course. Excellent facilities with an 85-station gym, two pools, sports hall, squash courts, aerobics studio and sauna.

LOUGHBOROUGH Rep Out Health & Fitness Club *15a High Street, Loughborough, Leicestershire LE11. Tel: 01509 260499* Yoga once at week. Pleasant gym. Sauna. You get your coffee at reception.

MARKET HARBOROUGH Harborough Leisure Centre *Northampton Road, Market Harborough, Leicestershire LE16. Tel: 01858 410115* Loads to do here. There is outdoor tennis as well as a sports hall. Pool for cooling down and a sauna and steam room for sweating it out. Lots of classes.

MELTON MOWBRAY Ragdale Hall Health Hydro *Ragdale Village, Ragdale, Melton Mowbray, Leicestershire LE14. Tel: 01664 434831 www.ragdalehall.co.uk* Grand stuff here with all you need at hand. Yoga throughout the day and every day too! Three pools, one outdoor. Aqua-aerobics. Great gym with full kit. Beauty therapy rooms, sauna, steam room and jacuzzi. Café and bar plus a veranda bar.

MELTON MOWBRAY Viniyoga East Midlands *Melton Mowbray. Tel: 01664 464852* Contact Sheila Baker.

OAKHAM Oakham Fitness Centre *Princess Avenue, Oakham, Leicestershire LE15. Tel: 01572 755556* Classes on offer include yoga, pilates and Power Chi yoga. Dance studio plus gym and sauna. Comfortable place. No café but everyone takes a water bottle anyway.

NORTHAMPTONSHIRE

BRACKLEY Brackley Recreation Centre *Springfield Way, Brackley, Northamptonshire NN13. Tel: 01280 701787* Good facilities including a gym, badminton courts, football, dance studio and yoga plus other exercise classes, sauna, steam room and sunbeds. Crèche.

CORBY Lodge Park Sports Centre *Shetland Way, Corby, Northamptonshire NN17. Tel: 01536 400033 www.corby.gov.uk* Nice place with regular general yoga classes, some sunbeds, a gym, badminton and table tennis, plus a crèche for the kids.

DAVENTRY Daventry Leisure Centre *Lodge Road, Daventry, Northamptonshire NN11. Tel: 01327 871144* A pleasant, well-equipped centre in this lovely old town. There are classes including yoga and a gym, pool, squash, badminton, coffee shop and crèche. Very friendly.

DAVENTRY Harpers Fitness Suite *Daventry Leisure Centre, Lodge Road, Daventry, Northamptonshire NN11.*

Tel: 01327 301382 www.harpersfitness.co.uk Another happy Harpers fitness place. We are growing fond of these. There is yoga twice a week, a pool, a studio with lots of classes, badminton, basketball, short tennis, squash courts and sunbeds. Crèche.

GREAT HOUGHTON YogaNorthants *Willow Cottage, 28 Willow Lane, Great Houghton, Northamptonshire NN4. Tel: 01604 766760 jonathantrapman@dial.pipex.com www.yoga northants.com* British Wheel of Yoga teacher Jonathan Trapman holds weekly classes of Hatha and Raja yoga for beginners through to intermediate students. Some weekend workshops and retreats in other UK venues and abroad.

KETTERING Kettering Leisure Village *Thurston Drive, Kettering, Northamptonshire NN15. Tel: 01536 414141* Facilities include gym, studio with yoga and other classes including aerobics, and a sauna.

NORTHAMPTON Derngate Gym & Fitness Club *9 Derngate, Northampton, Northamptonshire NN1. Tel: 01604 639248* A wide choice of classes including yoga. Gym, studio and crèche.

NORTHAMPTON Fitness First (Dallington) Ltd *Mill Lane, Dallington, Northampton, Northamptonshire NN5. Tel: 01604 751170 www.fitnessfirst.com* Part of the leisure chain and has most of the facilities they install as standard for their operation. Gym, exercise room, squash club and classes in Power yoga. There is a crèche, bar and restaurant. Go along and see if it's what you want for your money.

NORTHAMPTON Image & Unique Fitness Centre *22–23 Galowhill Road, Brackmills Industrial Estate, Northampton, Northamptonshire NN4. Tel: 01604 769009 www.imagegym.co.uk* Gym, studios for yoga, aerobics and other classes, and sauna.

NORTHAMPTON Inner Health School of Yoga *36 Glenfield Drive, Great Doddington, Northampton, Northamptonshire NN29. Tel: 01933 224963* Gail and Brian Cossera teach classes in Wellingborough and Northampton.

NORTHAMPTON Kingfisher Health Studio *1a Yelvertoft Road, Northampton, Northamptonshire NN2. Tel: 01604 710805* Yoga classes on a regular basis plus sauna, studio, toning beds and massages.

NORTHAMPTON Lings Forum *Weston Favell Centre, Northampton, Northamptonshire NN3. Tel: 01604 402833 www.northampton.gov.uk* Used by educational services during the day, Lings nevertheless has good facilities for non-students. The yoga is taught on a private teacher arrangement and there's a pool, gym, badminton, squash, aerobics and a spinning class.

NORTHAMPTON Moulton Leisure & Community Centre *Pound Lane, Moulton, Northampton, Northamptonshire NN3. Tel: 01604 670506* Gym, badminton and sauna. There is a children's club twice a week, which is a great idea – you can never start too young in keeping fit and making exercise part and parcel of your lifestyle. Bar.

NORTHAMPTON Overstone Park *Overstone, Northampton, Northamptonshire NN6. Tel: 01604 647666 info@overstonepark.co.uk www.overstonepark.co.uk* Part of a hotel complex, Overstone offers yoga classes plus a pool, gym, sauna, steam room, jacuzzi, beauty treatments and a bar and restaurant. Golf is available too.

RAUNDS Body Mind *Raunds. Tel: 01933 623706* Contact Annette Sykes

RUSHDEN Harpers Fitness Club *H E Bates Way, Rushden, Northamptonshire NN10. Tel: 01933 411635 www.harpersfitness.co.uk* Yoga classes plus pilates and other courses, dance studio, gym, cardio-vascular fitness equipment, sauna, sunbeds and crèche. Bar too.

TOWCESTER Towcester Centre for Leisure *Springfields, Towcester, Northamptonshire NN12. Tel: 01327 358188* Towcester is lucky in having such a large and well-provided leisure centre. The area around the place is also attractive and the nearby canal walkway offers a nice stretch for the legs. Yoga classes, two pools, gym, health suite, sauna and steam room, function room, a beautician who can be booked privately, and a crèche. Café. If only every local leisure centre was as pleasant as this.

WELLINGBOROUGH Salem Hall *Roade School, Roade, Wellingborough, Northamptonshire NN29. Tel: 01933 224963 GAIL@inner-healing.demon.co.uk* There are both day and evening yoga classes usually on offer here.

NOTTINGHAMSHIRE

GENERAL Friends of Yoga Society *Tel: 01159 7335435* Contact Pauline Mainland

BRAMCOTE Cynthia Marette for Yoga *Bramcote Memorial Hall, Church Street, Bramcote, Nottinghamshire NG5. Tel: 0115 953 4836*

CROPWELL BISHOP Beginners Yoga *Youth & Community Centre, Fern Road, Cropwell Bishop, Nottinghamshire NG12. Tel: 0115 933 5719 rogerra@ntlworld.com*

JACKSDALE Jacksdale Community Centre Yoga *Jacksdale Community Centre, Jacksdale, Nottinghamshire NG16. Tel: 01773 528264 LS@sole91.fsnet.co.uk www.soleinsights. co.uk*

KIMBERLEY Mix Ability Yoga *Kimberley Leisure Centre, Kimberley, Nottinghamshire NG15. Tel: 0115 955 0444* One and a half hour yoga sessions on a regular basis.

MANSFIELD Ravensdale Hall *Mansfield, Nottinghamshire NG19. Tel: 01623 471362 movingclouds@hotmail.com*

MANSFIELD WOODHOUSE Turner Hall Yoga *Turner Hall, Church Street, Mansfield Woodhouse, Nottinghamshire NG19. Tel: 01623 488059 Peter.whitlam@ntlworld.com*

NOTTINGHAM Burton Joyce Village Hall *Burton Joyce, Nottingham, Nottinghamshire NG14. Tel: 0115 920 6397*

NOTTINGHAM Expanded Yoga *Digby Avenue, Mapperley, Nottingham, Nottinghamshire NG15. Tel: 0115 955 0444* This is a yoga discussion group with a focus on integral asana. Give them a call and discuss the benefits of participating in the group. You may find it enlightening and interesting.

NOTTINGHAM Nottingham Tennis Centre *University Boulevard, Nottingham, Nottinghamshire NG7. Tel: 0115 970 1828 timfoyster@lineone.net* Enrol in advance here. Usually two yoga sessions each week.

NOTTINGHAM Yoga at Larksfield *Larksfield Junior School, Coronation Road, Watnay, Nottingham, Nottinghamshire NG15. Tel: 0115 955 0444* Mixed ability in two-hour session. Call to enrol before going.

NOTTINGHAM Yoga for Men *Claremont School, Claremont Road, Carrington, Nottingham, Nottinghamshire NG15. Tel: 0115 955 0444* Special yoga session for men only – one of the few such groups in the country.

WEST BRIDGFORD Cynthia Marette for Yoga *Gamston Community Hall, Gamston, West Bridgford, Nottinghamshire NG5. Tel: 0115 953 4836*

WOODTHORPE Good Shepherd Primary School *Somersby Road, Woodthorpe, Nottinghamshire NG5. Tel: 0115 920 6397* Twice-weekly gentle yoga classes. Beginners welcome.

OXFORDSHIRE

ABINGDON Whitehorse Leisure Centre *Bridge Street, Abingdon, Oxfordshire OX14. Tel: 01235 540700* Big place with all the facilities you might need including six outdoor tennis courts, ten indoor tennis courts, two squash courts and a badminton hall plus pool, sauna, steam room and sports therapists. Yoga classes on a regular basis. Crèche. Café and bar.

BANBURY Banbury Yoga Group *Spiceball Park Sports Centre, Spiceball Park, Banbury, Oxfordshire OX16. Tel: 01295 257522* Lots of yoga classes here from beginners onwards. The centre is well equipped and friendly with professional staff. Facilities on offer include a gym, badminton, squash, volleyball, football and table tennis, with a sauna, steam room, spa and beauty therapist available. Crèche. Café and bar. Check it out now. Contact Janice Pearse (01295 262412).

BECKLEY Stillness in Action *Beckley. Tel: 01865 351650* Contact Maarten Vermaag

DIDCOT Harpers Fitness Club *The Didcot Wave, Newlands Avenue, Didcot, Oxfordshire OX11. Tel: 01235 819666 www.harpersfitness.co.uk* Dynamic yoga and body balance on offer plus a pool and gym.

HENLEY-ON-THAMES Henley Indoor Sports Centre *Gillotts Lane, Henley-on-Thames, Oxfordshire RG9. Tel: 01491 577909* More than just your basics here. Health studio and gym, plus full range of classes including yoga, aerobics, aquagym and pilates. Sports massage. Beauty treatments. Crèche. Bar.

HENLEY-ON-THAMES Workshop Health & Fitness Club *Newtown Road, Henley-on-Thames, Oxfordshire RG9. Tel: 01491 414400 www.odyssey-group.co.uk* Pool, gym, sauna, sunbeds, crèche, bar and yoga classes. The pool has a retractable cover so it's an outside/inside affair.

IFFLEY Iffley Church Hall *Church Lane, Iffley Village, Oxford, Oxfordshire OX4. Tel: 01865 717373 katrina_billings@ lineone.net www.yogaoxford.co.uk* Take your mat and join the group, usually on a Monday.

KIDLINGTON Aviators Health & Fitness Club *Oxford Airport, Kidlington, Oxfordshire OX5. Tel: 01865 376600* No flying licence required to get in shape here. Gym, lots of classes in a nice studio, sports hall with badminton and squash. Crèche.

NUNEHAM COURTENAY Global Retreat Centre *Nuneham Park, Nuneham Courtenay, Oxfordshire OX44. Tel: 01865 343551* The Brahma Kumaris World Spiritual University operate this centre in a magnificent Palladian villa built by the Earl of Harcourt in 1756. George II called it, 'The most enjoyable place I know,' and Queen Victoria wrote after her visit, 'This is a most lovely place, with pleasure grounds in the style of Claremont.' About 15 minutes' drive from Oxford, the house is situated by the River Thames in 60 acres of land and gardens. The centre is staffed by teachers of meditation who are experienced in creating an atmosphere of peace and spirituality. As well as regular retreats lasting from one day to one week, a variety of seminars, workshops and courses offer a range of opportunities to learn meditation and yoga, develop personal skills and explore the common values essential to world harmony. These sessions include Knowing the Self, Exploring & Developing Meditation, Our External Relationship with God, and Spirituality in Daily Life. January and February are normally quiet months for programmes. Open all year. Facilities include garden, park and guest lounge. Everyone eats together. Vegetarian food. No alcohol allowed. No charges made but donations are welcome.

OXFORD Arena Fitness *109 Oxford Road, Cowley, Oxford,*

Oxfordshire OX4. Tel: 01865 779115 More a relaxation and toning facility than a fitness training centre. OK for yoga classes and you'll also find a sauna, steam room and sunbeds.

OXFORD Chinese Wu Hsing Buddhist Yoga *Oxford. Tel: 01865 245095* Contact Christopher Jones

OXFORD Esporta Health and Racquets Club *St Edward's School, Woodstock Road, Oxford, Oxfordshire OX2. Tel: 01865 318318 www.esporta.com* Claiming to be the leading leisure group in Britain, Esporta offers Oxford a really complete facility that we liked a lot. There are yoga classes plus loads more in the studio. Twenty outdoor tennis courts, squash, gym, pool, sauna, steam room and jacuzzi. Crèche. Café. It's very good, Esporta.

OXFORD Hugh Poulton Yoga *Oxford. Tel: 01865 340335 hughpoulton@btconnect.com* Ashtanga yoga classes for all levels. Daytime and evenings in north Oxfordshire.

OXFORD Ian Macdonald Yoga Group *70 Southmoor Road, Oxford, Oxfordshire OX2. Tel: 01865 516615 macdonald reynell@aol.com* Weekly group. Sometimes there are visiting teachers. Discuss details with Ian or send an SAE for info.

OXFORD Oxford Yoga Group *Tel: 01865 841018* Contact Gillian Webster

OXFORD Park Sports Centre *Holton, Oxford, Oxfordshire OX33. Tel: 01865 872128* Dance classes covering all styles and all age groups. Yoga classes plus gym, squash and badminton. Crèche. Café bar.

OXFORD Rivermead Rehab Centre *Abingdon Road, Oxford, Oxfordshire OX1. Tel: 01865 726119 yoga@innerbookshop.om* Suitable for beginners. A yoga class with emphasis on exploration and fun. Very friendly group. If you are interested in alternative spiritualities then visit the Inner Bookshop – also a lot of fun.

OXFORD Rupert Alison Yoga *Oxford rupert.alison@ ctsu.ox.ac.uk* Teacher trained with British Wheel of Yoga. Weekly classes, usually in the evening. Emphasis on fun and relaxation. Beginners and more advanced can join.

OXFORD The Yoga Garden *4 South Parade, Summertown, Oxford OX2. Tel: 01865 311300 mail@yogagarden.co.uk www.yogagarden.co.uk* Currently Oxford's only purpose-built yoga studio. Located in fashionable Summertown where the world-famous chef Raymond Blanc opened his first restaurant. Daily yoga classes are held on a drop-in basis and are suitable for beginners and more experienced practitioners. Most types of yoga are on offer including Iyengar, Ashtanga, Gentle, Integral and Flowing. Courses are held for complete beginners with no yoga experience. Founded in 2002, the studio affords comfort, hygiene and a touch of luxury. There is a sauna and plunge pool, use of which is included in the price of a yoga class. Changing rooms are right up to date with plenty of locker space, and a pilates room and three treatment rooms make this a busy, fun place. Treatments offered are from a wide range of complementary therapies including yoga massage, nutritional therapy, Alexander technique, acupuncture, chiropractic therapy and herbal medicine. Although there is a slightly disorganised feel about the establishment, the staff are friendly and professional and the teachers experienced. With excellent facilities, the Yoga Garden offers a complete experience for those who want lots of choices in one place. There is even an adjoining Italian restaurant called *Cibo!* where a good cup of coffee, a light lunch or a full supper can be taken. Not Raymond Blanc's inspired originality but very good anyway.

OXFORD Yoga with Mariella de Martini *Oxford. Tel: 01865 245893*

SUTTON COURTENAY The Abbey *Sutton Courtenay, Oxon OX14. Tel: 01235 847401 Fax: 01235 847608 Admin@theabbeysc.demon.co.uk* Now here is a *very* special place. The Abbey seeks to offer space, peace and support for individuals and groups who want to be still and find closer connection with the sacred dimension of life and with God. With its charming inner courtyard, flowers and surrounding meadow-like areas, this place has been going for a number of years and the community here is engaged in projects ranging from the dynamics of unemployment to the complementary relationship of men and women working in the ministry. The current community here is very small but dynamic, young, full of cheer and thoughtful. The programme of events is designed to encourage personal, social and ecological transformation and nourishment of our inner lives. There are many courses on offer, including yoga, Qigong and the Tree of Life, Tibetan healing exercises, the mysteries that lead us to Easter, music as the bridge of the soul, prayer retreats and a retreat on Sacred Economics: Spirit, Money, and Peace. This latter retreat asks some important questions such as, 'Can money be a commodity of spirit?' Open all year but sometimes closed for community needs. Camping possible. Facilities include a four-acre garden and library with Gandhi archive. Vegetarian food, taken alone or with the community. Self-catering in guesthouse. The Abbey is of archaeological importance because of the underlying Roman and Saxon remains. Location is quiet, in a village. Access: BR to Didcot Parkway, three miles away. Bus: No. 32 from Oxford runs every half-hour. Car: via A34.

THAME Racquets Fitness Centre *North Street, Thame, Oxfordshire OX9. Tel: 01844 261754 www.racquets-fitness-centre.com* Regular yoga class and a yoga relaxation class as well. Gym, aerobics, circuit training, racquetball, sauna and a crèche. Bar and restaurant. We liked it.

THAME Thame Leisure Centre *Oxford Road, Thame, Oxfordshire OX9. Tel: 01844 215607 thame@soll-leisure.co.uk* Ten-week yoga courses including Ashtanga yoga. Health suite, sauna and steam room plus spa, gym and pool. Just what your personal trainer ordered.

WALLINGFORD Abbey Sports Centre *Green Furlong, Berinsfield, Wallingford, Oxfordshire OX10. Tel: 01865 341035* Good centre with yoga classes, squash, football, sports hall, trampoline, pool and gym. Crèche available. Drinks machine.

WANTAGE Wantage Leisure Centre *Portway, Wantage, Oxfordshire OX12. Tel: 01235 766201 www.whitehorse.gov.uk* Excellent facility with yoga, gym, pool, squash, badminton, sports hall, netball, outdoor tennis, hockey . . . the lot! Sauna too. Bar.

WANTAGE Wantage Yoga Centre *Little Orchard House, Portway, Wantage, Oxfordshire OX12. Tel: 01235 765936 colin-george.brown@virgin.net* Mixed-ability yoga classes.

WITNEY Waters Edge Health Club *Downs Road, Witney, Oxfordshire OX8. Tel: 01993 778484* Pool, gym, aerobics studio with some 70 classes including yoga on offer. Sauna and steam. Crèche available nearby. Bistro.

SHROPSHIRE

ALBRIDGTON Albridgton Hall Health Leisure Club *Albridgton Hall Hotel, Albridgton, Shrewsbury, Shropshire SY4. Tel: 01939 291233* General yoga classes. Gym, pool, sauna and steam room. Squash. Beauty treatments. Coffee bar.

BROSELEY Bodylife Centre of Massage & Yoga *Spout Lane, Benthall, Broseley, Shropshire TF12. Tel: 01952 883135* Contact Derek Osborn. He holds classes in other parts of the county so ask what his current programme is.

HADLEY Hadley Castle Farm Community Centre *High Street, Hadley, Shropshire TF1. Tel: 01952 245983/642200 janetevansyoga@aol.com* Several classes on offer. Contact the teacher for details of current schedule. You can sometimes pay weekly and there may be concessions if you are over 60.

MADELEY Madeley Court Sports Centre *Court Street, Madeley, Telford, Shropshire TF7. Tel: 01952 680291* Weekly general yoga class. Fitness suite and pool. Bar in the evenings. No frills. Warm welcome.

MUCH WENLOCK Much Wenlock Leisure Centre *Farley Road, Much Wenlock, Shropshire TF13. Tel: 01952 727629* No great shakes but it's got the basics. Yoga classes plus pool and gym.

PONTESBURY Mary Webb School *Bogey Lane, Pontebury, Shrewsbury, Shropshire SY1. Tel: 01743 791742 cschiansky@ hotmail.com* Gentle yoga only. Lots of breathing and meditation included in classes.

SHAWBIRCH Shawbirch Community Centre *Oakfield Road, Shawbirch, Telford, Shropshire TF1. Tel: 01952 245983 janetevansyoga@aol.com* Pre-booking essential here with teacher Janet Evans. Several classes offered on a weekly basis. Take your yoga mat.

SHREWSBURY Castle Country Leisure Club *Halfway House, Shrewsbury, Shropshire SY5. Tel: 01743 884778* Good arrangement of yoga classes held both during the day and in the evenings. Two pools, gym, squash, tennis, sauna, steam room and jacuzzi. Bar serving food. Good place in one of the most attractive cities in the country.

SHREWSBURY Fitness First *112 St Michael's Street, Shrewsbury, Shropshire SY1. Tel: 01743 270272 www.fitness-first.com* Regular yoga class. Gym and nice studio for classes.

Aromatherapy. Sauna and steam room. Pool on the way. Join now and be ready.

SHREWSBURY Phoenix Health Studio *20a Mardol, Shrewsbury, Shropshire SY1. Tel: 01743 236165* General yoga class. Gym, sauna, spa and jacuzzi.

TELFORD Fitness First Gym *Stafford Court, Telford, Shropshire TF7. Tel: 01952 883135 derekosborn@cwcom.net www.fitnessfirst.com* Iyengar-style yoga. Weekly class. Discuss what you are looking for with teacher Derek Osborn. You can pay weekly. Take a mat. Derek uses a number of yoga styles and systems as his yoga teaching inspiration, including Iyengar and Ashtanga and systems from the Sivananda school. He is a British Wheel of Yoga member.

WELLINGTON Wellington Civic Centre *Wellington, Shropshire TF1. Tel: 01952 883135 derekosborn@cwcom.net* Weekly class. Take a mat. Pre-booking needed.

WELLINGTON Wellington Leisure Centre *Tan Bank, Wellington, Telford, Shropshire TF1. Tel: 01952 242048* Good place to go. Lots going on including a number of yoga classes, some for beginners and others for intermediate level. There is a gym, nice pool, sauna and steam facilities plus spa in the health suite. Body treatment area and massage available. Café. We like it.

STAFFORDSHIRE

BIDDULPH Biddulph Valley Leisure Centre *Lifestyle Health & Fitness Suite, Thames Drive, Biddulph, Stoke-on-Trent, Staffordshire ST8. Tel: 01782 297853 biddulphvalley@staffmorlands.gov.uk* Gym, pool, sports hall, badminton and other racquet sports. Crèche. Teacher comes in to give yoga classes.

BURTON-ON-TRENT Hoar Cross Hall Health Spa *Hoar*

Cross, Burton-on-Trent, Staffordshire DE13. Tel: 01283 575671 www.hoarcross.co.uk A grand stately home – check out the place on their website. You go for the day and enjoy the facilities which include a pool, gym, sauna, steam room, jacuzzi, tennis, croquet and yoga classes, and you also get a three-course buffet lunch. We think of this as a day retreat. It gives you a real chance to have a healthy break, relax and refresh.

BURTON-ON-TRENT Meadowside Leisure Centre *High Street, Burton-on-Trent, Staffordshire DE14. Tel: 01283 508865 www.eaststaffbc.gov.uk* One of the better centres with yoga, pool, gym, squash, badminton, short tennis and a crèche. Vending machine for drinks.

BURTON-ON-TRENT The New Image Health Studio *The Eyemex Business Park, Shodnall Road, Burton-on-Trent, Staffordshire DE14. Tel: 01283 561756* Basic place for fitness with yoga and t'ai chi, gym, aerobic studio and sunbeds.

CANNOCK Chase Leisure Centre *Stafford Road, Cannock, Staffordshire WS11. Tel: 01543 504065 www.cannock council.gov.uk* A local authority centre that makes you proud. Equipped with all you need including a pool, gym, sports hall with badminton and other racquet sports, aerobics classes, bowling green, sauna, steam room, sunbeds and a crèche. Café too. Usually about four yoga classes a week.

CANNOCK Club Fitness International *1st Floor, Danilo Court, High Green, Cannock, Staffordshire WS11. Tel: 01543 500001 www.westmids.co.uk/clubfitness/* More than the basics here in a nicely arranged facility with a downstairs restaurant. There are yoga classes, a main gym, spinning studio, aerobics studio, sauna, steam room, sunbeds and holistic therapy including massage. Coffee and tea. We liked it.

KEELE Keele University Leisure Centre *Keele, Newcastle, Staffordshire ST5. Tel: 01782 583368 www.keele.ac.uk* Hatha and Power yoga on offer along with a sports hall, gym and tennis courts.

LEEK Brough Park Leisure Centre *Ball Haye Road, Leek, Staffordshire ST13. Tel: 01538 373603 ghall@park-woodleisure.co.uk* Three or more yoga classes each week. Pool, gym, sports hall, spa and crèche. Bar. Good welcome here.

LEEK Fitness Factory *Britannia House, Salisbury Street, Leek, Staffordshire ST13. Tel: 01538 386306* A recent fire in the gym here forced a rethink and a refurbishment but the yoga classes continued. Bravo! We award this place a Gold Star for courage and hope you will go and check out the revised facility.

LEEK Haven Ladies Health & Fitness Club *Cross Street Mill, Leek, Staffordshire ST13. Tel: 01538 388288* This is strictly a women-only place. Yoga, pilates and other courses each week, weight training, sauna and a beauty salon. Bar.

LICHFIELD Lichfield Health & Fitness Club *Lorne House, Rotten Row, Lichfield, Staffordshire WS13. Tel: 01543 257704* Yoga, gym, sauna and jacuzzi. Not our cup of tea.

LICHFIELD 3 Spires Fitness *28 Bird Street, Lichfield, Staffordshire WS13. Tel: 01543 415653* This fitness centre plans to start yoga classes, so check it out.

RUGELEY Rugeley Adult Education *Taylors Lane, Rugeley, Staffordshire WS15. Tel: 01889 586423* Beginners, intermediate and advanced students taken in classes which approach yoga as a holistic system of practice involving physical, emotional and spiritual elements of self.

STAFFORD Stafford Yoga Group *Stafford, Staffordshire ST16. Tel: 01785 662207* Contact Irene Yates

STOKE-ON-TRENT Club Moativation *Festival Way, Stoke-on-Trent, Staffordshire ST1. Tel: 01782 202201 moathouse hotels.co.uk* Yoga and pilates both on offer. We confess that we are not usually as keen on hotel in-house fitness centres as we are on separate facilities, but this club is a good one. There is a heated pool, gym, studio for aerobics and other classes, a kids' playroom, sauna, steam room, jacuzzi and a beauty therapist on site.

STOKE-ON-TRENT Northwood Stadium *Keelings Rd, Northwood, Stoke-on-Trent, Staffordshire ST1. Tel: 01782 234400 www.stokeontrentcitycouncil.gov.uk* Three yoga classes a week, running track, squash, table tennis, netball and basket-ball.

STOKE-ON-TRENT South Moorlands Leisure Centre *Allen Street, Cheadle, Stoke-on-Trent, Staffordshire ST10. Tel: 01538 753331 www.leisure-centre.com.uk* The right place with the right equipment – pool, gym, aerobics, spinning classes, badminton, squash, sauna and classes in yoga. But be warned – the yoga is popular and there could be a waiting list. (You could wait in their nice café.)

STOKE-ON-TRENT Stoke Recreation Centre *Booth Street, Stoke-on-Trent, Staffordshire ST4. Tel: 01782 233433* Yoga leads at this centre with its gym, aerobics studio, squash and badminton. Crèche.

STOKE-ON-TRENT 21st Century Club *11 Davenport Street, Stoke-on-Trent, Staffordshire ST6. Tel: 01782 811698* Your basic place with yoga class, pool, gym, sauna and steam room. Bar.

TAMWORTH Peaks Leisure Centre *River Drive, Tamworth, Staffordshire B79. Tel: 01827 62008 www.peaksleisure centre.co.uk* Active, busy centre that gets you fit and relaxed with daily yoga classes, gym, pool, table tennis, sunbeds, jacuzzi, sauna and steam room. Quality stuff here.

UTTOXETER Uttoxeter Leisure Centre *Oldfields Road, Uttoxeter, Staffordshire ST14. Tel: 01889 562844* Facilities include pool, gym, aerobics studio, badminton and squash courts, yoga classes and crèche (but you must book it).

WARWICKSHIRE

COVENTRY Earlsdon Primary School *Earlsdon Avenue, Coventry, Warwickshire CV5. Tel: 02476 275552* Yoga on offer during term-time.

HENLEY IN ARDEN Henley in Arden Primary School *Arden Road, Henley in Arden, Warwickshire B95. Tel: 01527 857586 gillian@grussel.freeserve.co.uk*

LEAMINGTON SPA Mark Freeth Yoga *Leamington Spa, Tel: 01926 888556* Mark Freeth teaches Astanga Vinyasa yoga in Leamington Spa, Stratford-upon-Avon and Coventry throughout the week. Beginners courses, self-practice and full Vinyasa yoga teaching is available.

LEAMINGTON SPA Nautilus Health & Fitness Club *2 Spencer Street, Leamington Spa, Warwickshire CV31. Tel: 01926 831181* This club has a women-only gym as well as a regular fitness suite with circuit training. Hatha yoga on offer.

LEAMINGTON SPA Rachael White Yoga *Leamington Spa, Warwickshire CV32. Tel: 01926 337558 rwhitelspa@aol.com www.rachaelwhiteyoga.co.uk*

LEAMINGTON SPA Spirit Health & Fitness Club *58 Bedford Street, Leamington Spa, Warwickshire CV32. Tel: 01926 888180* Two kinds of yoga on offer here so discuss what systems and styles are currently being taught and which would be the right one for you. The facility is well equipped with a pool, gym, sauna, steam room, spa and studio.

RUGBY Dragons Health Club *Webb Ellis Road, Rugby, Warwickshire CV22. Tel: 01788 540523 www.dragons.co.uk* Two regular yoga classes usually on offer. Pool, gym, bar with food. Simple and to the point.

RUGBY Ken Marriot Leisure Centre *Trevor White Drive, Rugby, Warwickshire CV22. Tel: 01788 550303* A teacher comes in to give the yoga class here. The facilities include two pools, gym, sauna, steam room, massages, beauty treatments, squash, badminton and a café and bar. Nice place.

RUGBY Midland Yoga Centre *Rugby, Warwickshire CV21. Tel: 01788 330056 maurice_yoga@web-sights.co.uk www.web-sights.co.uk/yoga/*

SHIPSTON-ON-STOUR Shipston-on-Stour Village Hall *Shipston-on-Stour, Warwickshire CV36. Tel: 01608 6872319 bruce.singleton@virgin.net*

STRATFORD-UPON-AVON Club Moativation Health & Fitness *Queens Moat House, Stratford-upon-Avon, Warwickshire CV37. Tel: 01789 298128* Part of the hotel so you can use the bar and eat there. The fitness facilities include regular yoga classes, a pool, gym, sauna, steam room, jacuzzi, sunbed and beauty therapist.

STRATFORD-UPON-AVON Our Lady of Peace *Church Road, Stratford-upon-Avon, Warwickshire CV37. Tel: 01564 777969 michelleallen@knowle176.freeserve*

STRATFORD-UPON-AVON Stratford Leisure & Visitor Centre *Bridgefoot, Stratford-upon-Avon, Warwickshire CV37. Tel: 01789 268826* Check whether the yoga class is running in the current programme. Pool, gym, exercise studio, badminton, tennis, crèche and café.

STUDLEY The Gym *21b Alcester Road, Studley, Warwickshire B80. Tel: 01527 853754* Regular yoga classes plus gym, sauna, circuit training and aerobics.

WARWICK Ardencote Manor Hotel Leisure Club *Lye Green Road, Claverdon, Warwick, Warwickshire CV35. Tel: 01926 843872 www.ardencote.com/leisure/index.shtml* Power Chi yoga classes plus pool, two gyms, jacuzzi, sauna, steam room, outside whirlpool, four squash courts and aerobics on a regular basis. Two bars plus a big restaurant.

WOOTTON WAWEN Wooton Wawen Village Hall *Wootton Wawen, Warwickshire B95. Tel: 01527 857586 gillian@grussel.freeserve.co.uk* Antenatal yoga class which includes stretching, breathing, relaxation and preparation for labour and birth. There is also a postnatal class and a baby yoga course. (Check out the teachers' qualifications and experience and go to watch some of the classes before joining.)

WORCESTERSHIRE

WORCESTER Malvern Hills Yoga Centre *Tel: 01684 310884* Contact Gail Reeves

NORTHERN ENGLAND

CHESHIRE

GENERAL
Cheshire Yoga Teachers' Association
Tel: 0161 9738 319 Contact Christine Royle
Susan Rennie Yoga Iyengar Yoga *Tel: 01606 888324/01606 558252* susaniyengaryoga@yahoo.com Susan is a member of the Manchester and District Institute of Iyengar Yoga and holds around six classes every week.
The Yoga Circle *Tel: 0161 904 0588* Contact M. Priestner
ALTRINCHAM Altrincham Leisure Centre *Oakfield Road, Altrincham, Cheshire WA15. Tel: 0161 912 5900* Good facilities here – a gym, two pools, sauna, ladies' days, café and bar. Yoga and aerobics included in the various classes in the programme.
CHEADLE Cheadle Recreation Centre *Shiers Drive, Cheadle, Cheshire SK8. Tel: 0161 428 3216* Beginners and intermediate yoga classes plus gym, pool and sauna. Café area with drinks vending machine.
CHEADLE David Lloyd Leisure *Royal Crescent, Cheadle, Cheshire SK8. Tel: 0161 491 7402 www.davidlloydleisure.co.uk* Great place! Very professional but warm welcome for all. Hatha and Astanga yoga classes. Lots of family activities. Indoor and outdoor pools, indoor and outdoor tennis, squash and badminton courts. Massage, facials, sauna, steam room, jacuzzi. Café. Bar. Restaurant. Stay fit for ever, mate.
CHEADLE Village Hotel & Leisure Club *Cheadle Road, Cheadle, Cheshire SK8. Tel: 0161 428 0404* Hatha yoga suitable for all ages. This is a place to relax in and you could get just a wee bit lazy because there is a village pub and restaurants

on site. Gym, pool, sauna and steam room.

CHESTER Dragons Health Club *Wrexham Road, Chester, Cheshire CH4. Tel: 01244 683 999 www.dragons.co.uk* Yoga class, gym, pool, sauna, steam room and sunbeds plus a café restaurant with bar.

CHESTER Dutch Houses Fitness Centre Ltd *20 Bridge Street Row, Chester, Cheshire CH1. Tel: 01244 317515* Keeping its head just above basics, this place offers yoga, gym, saunas and some other mixed group classes. That's about it.

CHESTER Northgate Arena Leisure Centre *Victoria Road, Chester, Cheshire CH2. Tel: 01244 380444* One and a half hour Hatha yoga class during the day and in the evening. There is a good gym, pool, sauna, steam room, aerobics room and toning studio. Martial arts course. Café and bar.

CHESTER Total Fitness Chester *Liverpool Road, Chester, Cheshire CH2. Tel: 01244 393000 chestersales@totalfitness.org www.totalfitness.org* Morning and evening yoga classes. A good assortment of equipment and facilities here with two gyms, two pools, hydropool, sauna, steam room and solarium, plus a juice bar which serves salads. We liked it.

CONGLETON Impulse Fitness Suite *Congleton Leisure Centre, Worrall Street, Congleton, Cheshire CW12. Tel: 01260 271552* Once a week general yoga. A good get-fit facility here with two pools, fitness suite, sauna, sunbeds and crèche. Bar open in the evenings.

CREWE Hough Village Hall *Cobbs Lane, Hough, Crewe, Cheshire CW2. Tel: 01270 842043 Jim.Spencer@tesco.net*

CREWE Inches Aerobic Studios *Mill House, Brook Street, Crewe, Cheshire CW2. Tel: 01270 215022* Power Chi – a mix of t'ai chi and yoga. Gym, aerobics studio, ladies-only gym. Popular place. Pre-booking is recommended.

ELLESMERE PORT Cheshire Oaks Racquets &

Healthtrack Club *Stanney Lane, Ellesmere Port, The Wirral, Merseyside CH65. Tel: 0151 355 9050 gmcheshire@ therhg.co.uk* An above-average place. Hatha and general yoga classes, tennis, gym, indoor and outdoor pools, health and beauty suite, sauna and steam room, sunbeds, hairdresser and a restaurant. Welcome on board!

HUNTINGTON Old Hall Country Club & Spa *Old Hall Farm, Aldford Road, Huntington, Chester, Cheshire CH3. Tel: 01244 350873* All levels of yoga on offer here at this pleasant and efficient place. Gym, pool, tennis, sauna, steam room and beauty therapy salon. Lounge bar.

KNUTSFORD Active Images Leisure Club *Warford Park, Faulkners Lane, Knutsford, Cheshire WA1. Tel: 01565 880040* General yoga class at the moment, but this place is undergoing a big refurbishment so the already good facilities and surroundings should be great. Gym, pool, ladies' saunas, communal steam room, lots of other classes including aqua aerobics. Bistro. Crèche.

KNUTSFORD Knutsford Leisure Centre *Westfield Drive, Knutsford, Cheshire WA16. Tel: 01565 653321* Good place. General yoga class. Gym, sports hall, pool, health suite with sauna and steam room. Sunbeds. Outdoor tennis courts.

MACCLESFIELD Bollington Leisure Centre *Bollington, Macclesfield, Cheshire SK10. Tel: 01625 574774* Just the place to get started – not much more than the basics so no confusion of choice. Gym, yoga class, sauna and steam room to heat up, pool to cool off. Bar open three nights a week.

MACCLESFIELD Macclesfield Leisure Centre *Priory Lane, Macclesfield, Cheshire SK10. Tel: 01625 615602* Beginners and intermediate yoga classes. Pool, gym, football, badminton and squash on offer. Café. Bar.

MALPAS Oakcroft *Crosshill, Malpas, Cheshire SY14.*

Tel: 01948 860213 An organic garden place with established Soil Association affiliation. Vegetarian. Non-smoking.

NORTHWICH Dave's Gym & Sunbed Centre *Millbank, Off Station Road, Northwich, Cheshire CW9. Tel: 01606 330682* Morning yoga class plus a gym, fifteen sunbeds, aerobics, step and pilates classes. Free coffee and tea. A friendly and informal place.

ROMILEY Romiley Marina Pool *Hole House Fold, Romiley, Stockport, Cheshire SK6. Tel: 0161 430 3437* Really basic place. General yoga class on offer once a week, plus a gym, two pools, sauna and steam room.

RUNCORN Absolute Health & Fitness *207 Town Square, Halton Lea, Runcorn, Cheshire WA7. Tel: 01928 795000* A fairly complete workout facility here. Studio for activity classes including general yoga. A large mixed gym plus a women-only gym.

SALE Sale Leisure Centre *Broad Road, Sale, Cheshire M33. Tel: 0161 912 3360* Choose from mornings or evenings for your yoga class. The evening class is very busy and popular so you do need to book. Gym, pool, sauna and café.

SANDBACH FBI Gymnasium *Studd Green Farm, Dragons Lane, Sandbach, Cheshire CW11. Tel: 01270 753130* Beginners and intermediate yoga. Power yoga class. Gym and sunbeds. The salsa aerobic class is good. Drinks available from reception.

SANDBACH Sandbach Leisure Centre *Middlewich Road, Sandbach, Cheshire CW11. Tel: 01270 767129* Popular place so you must book in advance for your yoga class. Fitness room, pool, sauna and steam room, plus bar in the evenings.

SHAVINGTON Shavington Sports Centre *Rope Lane, Shavington, Crewe, Cheshire CW2. Tel: 01270 663221* General yoga classes on offer during the day and in the evenings. Gym, badminton, squash and tennis. Bar open in the evenings. Warm welcome. Popular place.

STOCKPORT Chestergate Suite *Sunwin House, Chestergate, Stockport, Cheshire SK1. Tel: 0161 336 5261*

STOCKPORT Hazel Grove Recreation Centre *Jacksons Lane, Hazel Grove, Stockport, Cheshire SK7. Tel: 0161 456 3467*

STOCKPORT The Lapwing Centre *Lapwing Lane, Stockport, Cheshire SK5. Tel: 0161 494 6465* No booking necessary – just drop in to the yoga class and try it out. There are two yoga classes each week. Facilities are good with a gym, fitness suite, sports hall, badminton, netball, table tennis and football. Bistro open during the day.

STOCKPORT LivingWell Health Clubs *Mudhurst Lane, Disley, Stockport, Cheshire SK12. Tel: 01663 766931 www.livingwell.co.uk* Here you get YogaBlast – the more energetic yoga. For those who want a gentler approach, there is also a Hatha yoga class. Pool, fully equipped gym, sauna, jacuzzi, relaxation room. Café.

STOCKPORT Mary Griffiths Yoga *Tel: 0161 427 4653 meedavid@cp.co.uk* Iyengar yoga taught in Stockport by a member of the Manchester & District Institute of Iyengar Yoga.

STOCKPORT Peel Moat Recreation Centre *Buckingham Road, Stockport, Cheshire SK4. Tel: 0161 442 6416* General yoga class. A few other classes on offer too. Fitness suite available. Basic but good.

STOCKPORT Stockport Library *Mino Hall, Stockport Central Library, Stockport, Cheshire SK1. Tel: 0161 336 5261 Yoga4nel@onetel.net.uk*

WARRINGTON Peter Clemson Yoga Warrington Area *Tel: 07944 566017*

WARRINGTON Total Fitness Warrington *Winwick Road, Warrington, Cheshire WA2. Tel: 01925 624900 warrington* *sales@totalfitness.org www.totalfitness.org* Excellent facility here. General yoga class. Women-only gym, main gym, two pools, hydrotherapy pool, sauna, steam room and sunbeds. A beauty salon, crèche and café complete the scene.

WARRINGTON Woolston Leisure Centre *Hall Road, Woolston, Warrington, Cheshire WA1. Tel: 01925 813939* Popular place in spite of rather limited facilities. Best to book for the evening yoga class but you can just turn up for the daytime class. Pool, gym, sauna and steam room.

WIDNES Body Tone Health & Fitness Studio *9 Everite Road Industrial Estate, Westgate, Widnes, Cheshire WA8. Tel: 0151 424 7059* Yoga, gym, jacuzzi, toning tables, lots of other classes. Drinks at reception. No-frills place.

WILMSLOW Total Fitness Wilmslow *Wilmslow Way, Handforth, Wilmslow, Cheshire SK9. Tel: 0161 440 9000 wilmslowsales@totalfitness.org www.totalfitness.org* Professional, friendly place with high standards. All levels of yoga from beginners to advanced, with Iyengar yoga offered for all. Gym, pool, three saunas, steam room, solarium, hydrotherapy pool. Healthy meals and non-alcoholic drinks available in the café.

WILMSLOW Viva Health & Leisure Clubs Ltd *Summerfield Village Centre, Dean Row Road, Wilmslow, Cheshire SK9. Tel: 01625 520555 info@viva.co.uk www.viva.co.uk/J script/wilmslow.html* Good, simple place. Yoga classes at all levels plus gym, pool, sauna and steam room. Café and bar.

WILMSLOW Wilmslow Circle of Yoga *Tel: 0161 432 5517* Contact Joan Thomson

WILMSLOW Wilmslow Leisure Centre *Rectory Fields, Station Road, Wilmslow, Cheshire SK9. Tel: 01625 533789* Yoga classes for all levels, daytimes and evenings. Nice gym and pool. Café.

WINSFORD Dingle Recreation Centre *High Street, Winsford, Cheshire CW7. Tel: 01606 552290* Not an inspiring place but it does have a yoga class.

CUMBRIA

GENERAL Awakenings *Tel: 01539 531672* Contact Christine Pickering

BURTON-IN-KENDAL You & Me Yoga Centre *Burton-in-Kendal. Tel: 01524 782103* Contact Maria Gunstone

CARLISLE Bodytek Fitness *Phoenix House, English Damside, Carlisle, Cumbria CA3. Tel: 01228 549435* All levels of yoga catered for in one class once a week. Large gym. Some women-only evenings.

DALTON-IN-FURNESS Dalton Leisure Centre *Chapel Street, Dalton-in-Furness, Cumbria LA15. Tel: 01229 463125* Intermediate yoga students only in the class held here. Pool, gym, sauna, café and bar.

KENDAL Kendal Leisure Centre *Burton Road, Kendal, Cumbria LA9. Tel: 01539 729777* All three standards of yoga catered for in this well-equipped place, where you will find a friendly and professional welcome. Small gym but OK equipment. 25-metre pool. Sports hall, badminton, squash, aerobics room, sauna, solarium. Café and bar.

LANCASTER Yoga Quests *Lancaster. Tel: 01524 381154* Contact Phillip Xerri

NEWBY BRIDGE Cascade Health & Fitness Club *Whitewater Hotel, The Lakelands Village, Newby Bridge, Cumbria LA12. Tel: 015395 31191 enquiries@whitewater hotel.co.uk www.whitewater-hotel.co.uk/leisure.html* Gym, pool, sauna, steam room and jacuzzi. General yoga suitable for all levels.

ULVERSTON Imago Fitness *Fell Street, Ulverston, Cumbria*

LA12. Tel: 01229 581642 www.imagofitness.co.uk General yoga on offer. Gym and big pool. Exercise room open to all, sunbeds and sauna. Nice café.

ULVERSTON South Lakes Yoga Teachers' Club *Ulverston.* Tel: 01229 861134 Contact Betina Mitchell

WHITEHAVEN Whitehaven Sports Centre *Flatt Walks, Whitehaven, Cumbria CA28.* Tel: 01946 695666 Yoga once a week plus a gym and steam room. Wide selection of other good-for-you activities and courses.

WINDERMERE Parklands Country Club *Kendal Road, Bowness-on-Windermere, Windermere, Cumbria LA23.* Tel: 01539 444640 What's on offer is reasonable for a country club. With general yoga classes for all levels, gym, pool, sauna, steam room, sunbeds and a bar, it's a pleasant place to be.

DURHAM AND TYNE & WEAR

GENERAL

Kripalu Yoga Support Group *North Shields.* Tel: 0191 257 0988 Contact Muriel McLacland

North East Institute of Iyengar Yoga *Seaburn Dene.* Tel: 0191 548 7457 Contact Gordon Austin

CHESTER-LE-STREET Riverside Health Club *County Durham Cricket Club Riverside, Chester-le-Street, Durham DH3.* Tel: 0191 387 2814 General yoga class that tries to bring yoga into your life as part of mind and body wellbeing. Sports hall, tennis courts, bistro and bar.

CROOK Spectrum Leisure Complex *Hunwick Lane, Willington, Crook, Durham DL15.* Tel: 01388 747000 Rather male-orientated place with snooker, sports hall, badminton and exercise circuit classes. But there is yoga on offer too.

DARLINGTON Darlington Yoga Group *Tel: 01325 730092.* Contact Vera Oates

DARLINGTON The Dolphin Centre *Horse Market, Darlington, Durham DL1. Tel: 01325 388406* Drop-in yoga class, plus a general-ability yoga course (you need to apply for this). Pool and plenty of other classes available. Café.

DARLINGTON Penthouse Fitness Suite *86–88 Skinnergate, Darlington, Durham DL3. Tel: 01325 353637* Practical and to-the-point fitness place – yoga once a week plus gym and sauna.

DURHAM Abbey Sports Centre *Abbey Road, Durham DH1. Tel: 0191 383 1199* General-ability yoga classes. Also a basic yoga course that runs for six weeks at a time. Additional facilities include a gym, sauna and steam room.

DURHAM Deerness Sports Centre *Valley View, Ushaw Moor, Durham DH7. Tel: 0191 373 2324* Yoga class once a week plus gym and sauna. Just your basic facility here. Take your water bottle.

DURHAM Meadowfield Sports Centre *John Street North, Meadowfield, Durham DH7. Tel: 0191 378 9888* Sports hall, badminton, and yoga once a week.

NEWTON AYCLIFFE Newton Aycliffe Leisure Centre *Beveridge Arcade, Newton Aycliffe, Durham DL5. Tel: 01325 300500* Gym, pool, sauna and steam room. Yoga class once a week. Bar open in the evenings.

NEWTON AYCLIFFE Oak Leaf Sports Complex *School Aycliffe Lane, Newton Aycliffe, Durham DL5. Tel: 01325 300600* Good place with a sports hall, badminton, squash, bowls, aerobics and regular yoga classes. Restaurant and bar.

PETERLEE Jupiter Health & Fitness Centre *Seaside Lane, Easington, Peterlee, Durham SR8. Tel: 0191 527 2576* All-levels yoga class in a great facility. Two gyms, aerobics room, sauna, sunbeds and toning tables. No café, though, so you'll have to pack your water bottle.

SHERBURN Sherburn Sports Centre *Front Street, Sherburn, Durham DH6. Tel: 0191 372 1121* Hatha yoga and general yoga classes available. Gym and sports hall plus badminton and football. Drinks machine.

SHILDON Shildon Sunnydale Leisure Centre *Middridge Lane, Shildon, Durham DL4. Tel: 01388 777340* Yoga class once a week and a fitness suite where you can limber up. Lots of other classes. Sauna and sunbed.

STANLEY Louisa Centre *Front Street, Stanley, Durham DH9. Tel: 01207 218877* Weekly yoga during the day. Gym. Pool on its way. Simple place but an improver.

LANCASHIRE

GENERAL Lancashire Yoga Teachers' Association *Oswaldtwistle. Tel: 01254 381325* Contact Irene O'Meara

BOLTON Esporta Health & Fitness *Unit 2 Waters Meeting Road, Bolton, Lancashire BL1. Tel: 01204 360400 www.esporta.com* Membership club and part of the national Esporta Leisure Group. Yoga for strength and relaxation on offer with various classes during the week plus a lot of pilates sessions. The membership is a package price so you get the classes, gym, pool and loads more.

BOLTON Farnworth Health Club *Gladstone Road, Farnworth, Bolton, Lancashire BL4. Tel: 01204 572921* A helpful and welcoming leisure club. Busy, popular and full of facilities and classes. Not just various yoga courses but about 40 other classes as well. There is no joining fee but you need to take out membership. Ladies-only club, gym, pool, sauna, TV lounge, stretch 'n' tone course and a café.

BURNLEY Bodywise *Market Hall, Market Square, Burnley,*

Lancashire B11. Tel: 01697 322478 Popular place with regular yoga class, sunbeds, sauna, steam room, gym and spinning bikes. Crèche on certain days of the week. Aerobics sometimes available.

BURNLEY Classic World of Fitness *Exhibition Centre, Parker Lane, Burnley, Lancashire BB11. Tel: 01282 412800* Yoga, aerobics, gym. Go, do it, go home.

BURY Jubilee Centre *Mosley Avenue, Bury, Lancashire BL9. Tel: 0161 763 9030* Yoga for the over 50s here. Art, music and dancing classes. No fitness facilities.

BURY LA Fitness *Chapel Street, Tottington, Bury, Lancashire BL8. Tel: 0161 764 6177 www.lafitness.co.uk* A mixed class combining yoga, pilates and t'ai chi several times a week.

BURY Stables Fitness & Leisure Club *Walshaw Road, Bury, Lancashire BL8. Tel: 0161 763 9999* The Stirrups Café is where you go after the yoga class, pool, gym, whirlpool, sauna and steam room. Ah!

CHORLEY Ashley Park *1–3 Park Road, Chorley, Lancashire PR7. Tel: 01257 414888* Good studio for yoga and other fitness and exercise classes. Gym and sauna. Basic and direct and we like it.

CHORLEY Clayton Green Sports Centre *Clayton Green Road, Clayton-le-Woods, Chorley, Lancashire PR6. Tel: 01257 515050* Concerned staff in a good facility. General yoga and Power yoga are both on offer, but this is a busy and popular place so you need to book. Gym, tennis and badminton complete the picture.

CLITHEROE Lee Carter Leisure *Off Lowergate, Clitheroe, Lancashire BB7. Tel: 01200 424472* Two yoga sessions each week. Dance studio, gym, pool and beauty therapy. Nice place.

CLITHEROE Roefield Leisure Centre *Edisford Road,*

Clitheroe, Lancashire BB7. Tel: 01200 442188 Helpful and pleasant staff. No pool but a gym, sports hall, aerobics, short tennis and badminton.

DARWEN Darwen Leisure Centre & Pool *The Green, Darwen, Lancashire BB3. Tel: 01254 771511* Yoga class plus pilates, gym, pool, sauna and crèche. Café.

HEYWOOD Fitness Connection *6 Bethel Street, Heywood, Lancashire OL10. Tel: 01706 360383* Another good place in Lancashire with yoga classes on a regular basis, a gym, aerobics studio, sauna, steam room, sunbeds and a crèche run during certain days of the week.

HEYWOOD Heywood Fitness Centre *49 Bridge Street, Heywood, Lancashire OL10. Tel: 01706 622006* Hatha yoga and a gym. Pool across the road. Sauna mainly used by men.

LANCASTER St Leonardsgate Yoga Studios *98 St Leonardsgate, Lancaster LA1. Tel: 01524 34054 dreamyoga@ freeuk.com* Yoga teacher Pat Benson offers classes at the studios and elsewhere. Call and ask her what is available and discuss what you want to do in yoga.

LANCASTER V.V.V. Health & Leisure Club *The Shore, Hest Bank, Lancaster, Lancashire LA2. Tel: 01524 823363* A fun place where you can leave the kids for a supervised play session as well as use a normal crèche. There is not just a regular gym but also a rehab gym along with a pool, sauna, sunbeds and about six yoga classes every week. We liked this place.

LYTHAM ST ANNES Lytham YMCA *Mythop Road, Lytham St Annes, Lancashire FY8. Tel: 01253 739166* The YMCAs have got it pretty much right when it comes to how they run their set-ups – but then they have been going for many years. Here is another good one, with yoga classes, gym, snooker, body conditioning, badminton, tennis, circuit training and classes for the kids. Go YMCA – we would!

OLDHAM Body Matters 72 High Street, Lees, Oldham, Lancashire OL4. Tel: 0161 652 6585 Basic stuff here – yoga, gym and women-only sauna.

OLDHAM Tara Sports & Leisure Grains Road, Shaw, Oldham, Lancashire OL2. Tel: 01706 841460 Mixed-level yoga classes, aerobics, step class, circuit training, gym and steam room.

OSWALDTWISTLE Hath Yoga Classes Oswaldtwistle, Lancashire. Tel: 012254 396182 jyhill@hotmail.com Hatha yoga classes on a regular basis with teacher Julie Hill.

PRESTON Body Logic Eden Street, Leyland, Preston, Lancashire PR5. Tel: 01772 456161 A Lancashire basic here with yoga classes, gym and sauna.

PRESTON Brooklands Country House Health Farm Bruna Hill, Barnacre, Preston, Lancashire PR3. Tel: 01995 605162 Membership needed here but they will encourage you to see what's on offer before you join. The facilities are excellent, with Astanga yoga classes plus other courses, a gym, hydro-pool, indoor swimming pool, steam room, aerobics and relaxation lounges. Worthy of a check-out.

PRESTON Garstang Leisure Centre Windsor Road, Garstang, Preston, Lancashire PR3. Tel: 01995 605410 Line dancing here as well as yoga classes. There is Hatha and general yoga and beginners are welcomed. Facilities not much to write home about.

PRESTON Just For Ladies The Centre, Hill Street, Preston, Lancashire PR1. Tel: 01772 558808 Yoga, gym, steam room, toning tables, sunbeds, aerobics and a running club.

PRESTON Leyland Leisure Centre Lancaster Gate, Leyland, Preston, Lancashire PR5. Tel: 01772 424729 Yoga classes in ten-week courses, pool, gym, squash, badminton, and a crèche on some days.

PRESTON Penwortham Leisure Centre *Crow Hills Road, Penwortham, Preston, Lancashire PR1. Tel: 01772 747272* Penwortham Leisure Centre really does have everything you need in a leisure centre, with a gym, pool, aerobics, judo, badminton, netball, football, tennis and lots of yoga classes including one for the over 50s. Crèche too on some days.

PRESTON Preston Marriott Leisure Club *418 Garstang Road, Broughton, Preston, Lancashire PR3. Tel: 01772 863858* Membership necessary for a club that has yoga classes, gym, pool, health and beauty salon and a bar.

PRESTON Ribby Hall Leisure Village *Ribby Road, Wrea Green, Preston, Lancashire PR4. Tel: 01772 671111* Ribby Hall is high on our list of best places. It is friendly and efficient with excellent facilities. There are regular yoga classes, but you also get a gym, badminton, squash, tennis, pool, sauna, steam room, jacuzzi, beauticians waiting to transform you and a crèche for the kids. Bistro for relaxation and chatting to friends.

PRESTON Westview Leisure Centre *West View, Preston, Lancashire PR1. Tel: 01772 796788* Basic centre with yoga, pool, gym, sauna and steam room. Crèche during the day.

ROCHDALE Fitness for Life *Caldershaw Centre, Ings Lane, Rochdale, Lancashire OL12. Tel: 01706 715690* Ladies gym, regular gym, toning tables, sauna, steam room, jacuzzi, spa and yoga classes. Crèche on certain days and some evenings.

ROSSENDALE The Sports Centre *Helmshore Road, Haslingden, Rossendale, Lancashire BB4. Tel: 01706 227017* Just a gym place but yoga classes are on offer.

TODMORDEN Yoga with Michael Taylor & Elisabeth Wilson *Todmorden. Tel: 01706 818299/07979 954349 astanga@owlers.demon.co.uk* Based on the Lancashire and Yorkshire borders, these teachers give Astanga yoga classes to both beginners and intermediates. Classes are usually in Todmorden and Nelson.

WIGAN Abbey Lake Sports Centre Ltd *Orrell Road Orrell, Wigan, Lancashire WN5. Tel: 01695 633445* Nice outfit here and warm welcome from all. Yoga classes, gym, pool, cardio-vascular sports, sauna, steam room, jacuzzi and sunbeds.

WIGAN Body Image Fitness Centre *1 Swan Lane, Hindley, Wigan, Lancashire WN2. Tel: 01942 746800* Astanga yoga on a weekly basis plus lots of facilities including a pool, mixed gym, ladies gym, cardio-vascular room, sauna, sunbeds and beauty and massage treatments.

WIGAN Total Fitness Wigan *Warrington Road, Goose Green, Wigan, Lancashire WN3. Tel: 01942 326800 wigansales@ totalfitness.org www.totalfitness.org* Gym, pool, aerobics, pilates and yoga. Members only.

GREATER MANCHESTER

ATHERTON Wigan Metrosport *DSO Howe Bridge, Ekersley Fold Lane, Atherton, Manchester M46. Tel: 01942 870403 www.activelifeservices.org.uk* Two yoga classes plus fitness hall, pools, squash, sports hall, table tennis and bar.

CADISHEAD Cadishead Community Hall *Cadishead, Manchester M30. Tel: 0161 336 5261 Yoga4nel@onetel.net.uk* This is a drop-in class and there are other classes held in the area so ring the teacher (Ted) and find the one closest to you.

CHORLTON Ananda Marga Centre *42 Keppel Road, Chorlton, Manchester M21. Tel: 0161 282 9224 Anandamarga. mcr@gmx.net www.anandamarga.org* The Indian philosopher, teacher and poet P. R. Sarkar founded the Ananda Marga movement. Yoga and meditation are taught and practised as methods for self-development and self-realisation, while social service is emphasised and an outward expression of developing the human potential. The centre is in a Victorian terraced house in south Manchester. Quiet, informal and friendly, there are classes in yoga posture and regular meetings for meditation. Creative writing and painting workshops are offered. There are evenings of inspirational singing, music and poetry.

CHORLTON St Clements Church *Edge Lane, St Clements Road, Chorlton, Manchester M21. Tel: 0161 881 5300/07740 434612 www.rishiculture@hotmail.com* Eight-week course suitable for beginners usually on offer.

CHORLTON St Ninian's Church *Wilbraham Road, Chorlton, Manchester M21. Tel: 0161 881 5300/07740 434612 www.rishiculture@hotmail.com* Several yoga classes each week. Gentle yoga is emphasised. Beginners welcome. Introductory class for those considering yoga for the first time.

CHORLTON Yoga for You *Chorlton, Manchester M21. Tel: 0161 881 5300/07740 434612 www.rishiculture@hotmail.com* Small group instruction and one-to-one teaching in your home or at the teacher's place. Call and discuss what is on offer and the current fees.

MANCHESTER Finesilver & Morgan Hatha Yoga *Manchester. Tel: 07740 434612 rishiculture@hotmail.com* Classical Hatha yoga in Manchester with Suzanne Finesilver and Ken Morgan.

MANCHESTER LivingWell Health Club *Sunlight House, Quay Street, Manchester M3. Tel: 0161 832 3227 www. livingwell.co.uk* Weights and gym, pool, yoga classes, sunbeds, sauna, meals and a bar. Nice place, good welcome, friendly staff.

MANCHESTER Manchester Buddhist Centre *16–20 Turner Street, Northern Quarter, Manchester M4. Tel: 0161 834*

9232 *info@manchesterbuddhistcentre.org.uk www.manchester buddhistcentre.org.uk* An old Victorian warehouse right in the heart of Manchester city centre, sensitively restored and now a Buddhist centre offering classes. Exposed brick and natural wood contribute to an atmosphere of calm while the integrity of architecture, building materials and voluntary human effort has created an inspiring place. An example of what the new vibrant Manchester is all about. There are two shrine halls. The larger one is for groups and the smaller for private meditation or prayer. Upstairs in the natural health centre, Bodywise, is where yoga is on offer in a spacious studio. You can also enrol for Qigong or make a date for massage, reflexology, pain management, acupuncture and shiatsu in the modern treatment rooms. Introductory classes are offered in meditation and Buddhism. To complete the facility there is a bookshop and reference library and the award-winning vegan Earth Café – a haven for healthy eating and drinking.

MANCHESTER Manchester & District Institute of Iyengar Yoga Contact Janice Yates. *Tel: 0161 368 3614*

MANCHESTER Mike Nevitt Yoga *South Manchester. Tel: 0161 445 8560/0161 438 0148 Janice.roscoe@virgin.net* Mysore-style yoga classes. All levels of yoga taught.

MANCHESTER Powerhouse Gym *12 Amos Street, Manchester M9. Tel: 0161 205 9596* Gym, squash, badminton, football, multi-gym facility, yoga class.

MANCHESTER YogaSpace *Basement Studio, 35/37 Thomas Street, Manchester M4. Tel: 0161 288 6918 www.yogaspace. org.uk* In the basement of a Creative Design shop in a quiet street in the centre of this great city. Founded in 2001, YogaSpace is a relatively new centre and the first in central Manchester. Evening and day classes and courses in many styles of yoga are on offer. All teachers are accredited and the director of the studio invites only those teachers who have a strong understanding of the spiritual dimension of yoga as well as a high proficiency in the physical postures and movements. Yoga retreats are planned for Cumbria, as is a residential centre in Spain. They also hope to develop therapeutic yoga for healing.

MIDDLETON Bobby Charlton Health & Fitness Centre *Hopwood Hall, Rochdale Road, Middleton, Manchester M24. Tel: 0161 653 2070 www.hopwood.ac.uk* A new facility carrying a very famous name in sport. The yoga class is very popular and the facilities are excellent. In addition to the fitness suite, which has all the latest equipment, there is badminton, tennis (on grass courts), aerobics studio, sauna and steam room, and a physiotherapy clinic. Well worth going along.

MIDDLETON Lancashire Health & Racquets Club *Heywood Old Road, Middleton, Manchester M24. Tel: 0161 653 4567 www.esporta.com* Lots of yoga on offer here including Astanga. Also pilates and t'ai chi. Run by the Esporta group, there are indoor and outdoor pools, tennis, squash, badminton, sauna, steam room and jacuzzi. Restaurant and bar.

MIDDLETON Middleton Recreation Centre *Fountain Street, Middleton, Manchester M24. Tel: 0161 643 2894 www.rochdale.gov.uk* This council facility has loads to offer everybody. There are a number of classes including yoga of various types plus two pools, gym, aerobics, spinning studio, squash courts and a bar. We liked it a lot!

NORTHENDEN Northenden County Primary School *Bazley Road, Northenden, Manchester M22. Tel: 07776 236755 yvette@sand28.freeserve.co.uk* Yoga classes where you pay by the session. Usually held weekly in the evening.

PARTINGTON Partington Leisure Centre *Chapel Lane,*

Partington, Manchester M31. Tel: 0161 912 5430 50+yoga class only. There is a fitness suite, gym, pool and sports hall.

RADCLIFFE Dynamics *166 Water Street, Radcliffe, Manchester M26. Tel: 0161 724 5900* Hatha yoga class. Gym, studio for yoga and other classes, boxing and sunbeds.

SALFORD Broadwalk Library *Broadwalk, Salford, Manchester M6. Tel: 0161 792 3029 rita.sue.fisher@ ntlworld.com* Peaceful friendly atmosphere where the yoga class places a focus on relaxation and getting rid of stress. Beginners welcome.

TRAFFORD PARK David Lloyd Leisure Centre *Barton Embankment, Trafford Park, Manchester M17. Tel: 0161 749 2000 www.davidlloydleisure.co.uk* Great facility here with yoga classes including Astanga and Hatha. Gym, pool, racquet sports, sauna and refreshments. Go for it!

URMSTON High Level Fitness Club *47 Higher Road, Urmston, Manchester M41. Tel: 0161 747 2525* Yoga classes on regular offer, cardio-vascular training suite, workout equipment, boxing, sauna, massage and reflexology.

WHITEFIELD Whitefield Yoga Group *Tel: 0161 766 2305* Contact Pauline O'Gara

MERSEYSIDE

GENERAL Merseyside Yoga Association *Tel: 0151 652 6343* Contact Janet Irlam

BIRKENHEAD Fern Park Health & Leisure Club *17 Oxton Road, Birkenhead, Merseyside L41. Tel: 0151 653 4744* A members-only place with general yoga classes. Facilities include a gym and sauna. That's about it.

BOOTLE Bootle Stadium Sports Centre *Maguire Avenue, Bootle, Merseyside L20. Tel: 0151 523 4212* Yoga classes. Gym. Sports hall. Badminton. Bar. Go, do it, feel great, go home.

BROMBOROUGH Village Hotel & Leisure Club *Pool Lane, Bromborough, The Wirral CH62. Tel: 0151 643 1616 paul.dagnall@village-hotels.com www.merseyworld.com/ villagehotel/leisure.html* Yogalates class which is a combination of yoga and pilates. Regular yoga class too. Nice pool. Squash and tennis facilities. Aerobics. Jacuzzi, sauna and steam room. Café and bar.

HUYTON The Huyton Leisure Centre *Roby Road, Huyton, Liverpool, Merseyside L36. Tel: 0151 443 3786* Straightforward centre with yoga, gym, pool, sauna and a drinks machine. Maybe the future holds more?

LIVERPOOL Body Talk North West Ltd *580 Longmoor Lane, Liverpool L10. Tel: 0151 525 1134* Weekly evening yoga class. Gym, sauna, sunbed and some other classes. Your basic outfit here.

LIVERPOOL Cheshire Lines Health & Fitness Centre Leisure Complex *Sefton Lane, Liverpool L31. Tel: 0151 531 7777* Lovely hot-tub facility here with a good programme of classes including yoga. Mixed gym and a women-only gym plus a full-size swimming pool where you can do aqua aerobics. Sauna too.

LIVERPOOL Everton Park Sports Centre *Great Homer Street, Liverpool L5. Tel: 0151 207 1921* General yoga plus a 50+ class. Nice pool, good sports hall, gym, squash court. Steam room. No café but a lounge area.

LIVERPOOL Hearts Health Club *5 Little Crosby Road, Crosby, Liverpool, Merseyside L23. Tel: 0151 924 0004* Free tea and coffee. Yoga class, gym and 'wet suite' – sauna, steam room and jacuzzi.

LIVERPOOL Lady In Leisure *21–25 Bold Street, Liverpool L1. Tel: 0151 709 1800* General yoga class plus some others. Gym, sauna and coffee area.

LIVERPOOL Picton Sports Centre *Wellington Road, Wavertree, Liverpool L15. Tel: 0151 734 2294* Picton Sports Centre offers good general yoga classes, a gym and a drinks vending machine. Nothing else is on offer so get started with the yoga class before they decide to shut up shop completely.

LIVERPOOL Tone Zone 2 *The Cloisters, Formby, Liverpool L37. Tel: 01704 872727* A studio for yoga and other classes and courses. Gym, sauna, steam room and spa. Free tea and coffee. A good welcome.

LIVERPOOL Total Fitness Liverpool *Binns Road, Edge Lane Retail Park, Liverpool L13. Tel: 0151 252 6200* edge lanesales@totalfitness.org www.totalfitness.org A good centre with much to offer. Gym, women-only gym, a 25-metre pool, hydrotherapy suite, sauna, steam room and spa facility. Beauty salon and studio as well. Tasty juice bar. Compliments are in order.

LIVERPOOL Universal Fitness Studio *First Floor 249–251 Walton Road, Liverpool L4. Tel: 0151 284 8581* Fully equipped gym. Sauna and steam room. Yoga classes. Café and bar.

LIVERPOOL Walton Sports Centre *Walton Hall Avenue, Liverpool L4. Tel: 0151 523 3472* Yoga classes twice a week. A fully equipped gym plus other classes. No frills but pleasant and all you need to get started for fitness and relaxation.

NEW BRIGHTON Comprehensive Yoga Fellowship *Tel: 0151 639 9402* Contact Gordon Smith

ST HELENS LivingWell Health Club *13 Ackers Lane, St Helens, Merseyside WA10. Tel: 01744 22131* www.livingwell. co.uk LivingWell Health Club offers a gym, sauna, steam room and spa plus general activities and classes including yoga. Café.

ST HELENS Ruskin Leisure Gym *Ruskin Drive, Dentons Green, St Helens, Merseyside WA10. Tel: 01744 454494* Yoga class. Gym. Pool. Jacuzzi, sauna and steam room. Members bar.

SEFTON Total Fitness Sefton *Northern Perimeter Road, Switch Island, Sefton, Liverpool, Merseyside L30. Tel: 0151 527 3600 marketing@totalfitness.org www.totalfitness.org* Here we go again with Total Fitness – and again a nice place. General yoga class plus a grand pool, hydrotherapy pool, sauna, sunbeds and loads of other classes. Café bar. We liked it.

SOUTHPORT Dragons Health Club *Marine Drive, Southport, Merseyside PR8. Tel: 01704 532999 www.dragons.co.uk* No waiting here – just pop in and start getting fit. Buy a ticket and go to yoga, the gym, swim in the pool, use the steam room... If bored after all that, go to the beauty treatment room and refresh. Café and bar.

SOUTHPORT Victoria Sports & Leisure Club *Prom, Southport, Merseyside PR9. Tel: 01704 541220* Large, well-equipped club, with various classes including yoga. There are three pools, a mixed gym and a women-only gym. A couple of saunas plus two steam rooms and two jacuzzis. Café and bar.

THORNTON HOUGH Thornton Hall Country Health Club *Thornton Hall Hotel, Neston Road, Thornton Hough, The Wirral, Merseyside L63. Tel: 0151 353 0116* Members only. General yoga and other classes, gym, swimming pool, beauty spa, sauna, steam room and two outdoor hot-tubs. Café and bar. Extremely pleasant and relaxing.

WALLASEY Hearts Health Club *136–142 Wallasey Road, Wallasey, Merseyside L44. Tel: 0151 639 7781* Hatha and Astanga yoga on offer along with pilates classes. Nice gym. Sauna and jacuzzi. Free tea and coffee. Relaxed place.

WHISTON Logwood Leisure Club *Whiston Works, Fallows Way, Whiston, Prescot, Merseyside L35. Tel: 0151 480 5678* A fairly complete leisure place with regular yoga classes, a gym, pool, sauna, steam room, jacuzzi, toning tables and sunbed.

Café, bar and restaurant. Watch the balance between your exercise and your food and drink consumption amidst the conviviality.

THE WIRRAL Fitness First (Wirral) Ltd *Welton Road, Croft Business Park, The Wirral, Merseyside L62. Tel: 0151 346 1100 www.fitnessfirst.com* Fitness is first here with yoga classes, a gym, sauna and steam room, aromatherapy and a nice bar. Pleasant place.

THE WIRRAL Leasowe Recreation Centre *Twickenham Drive, The Wirral, Merseyside L46. Tel: 0151 677 0916* Weekly yoga class. With two pools and a small fitness suite, this is sufficient to meet your exercise needs – but no luxury touches. Small café.

THE WIRRAL Oval Sports Centre *Old Chester Road, Bebington, The Wirral, Merseyside L63. Tel: 0151 645 0596* No need to book your yoga here – just go along. There are two large pools in which to float and relax, a large gym for your workout, then a café for that coffee and snack.

THE WIRRAL Physical Fitness Studios Ltd *The Mount, Heswall, The Wirral, Merseyside L60. Tel: 0151 342 7300* Two gyms here, one for the mixed crowd and the other just for the ladies. A sauna, sunbeds and coffee lounge complete the picture. Nice.

NORTHUMBERLAND

GENERAL Northumberland Yoga Group *Tel: 01670 787423* Contact Betty Websell

ASHINGTON Oasis Health Club *18 Woodhorn Road, Ashington, Northumberland NE63. Tel: 01670 854367* Excellent facility and programme here. First off there are different classes on offer including Power Chi yoga, which mixes t'ai chi with yoga systems. Relaxation is part of the close of each session so you go away really destressed and unloaded. There is a women-only gym and a sauna. Sunbed and beauty therapy are also available. T'ai chi and other classes in a wide-ranging programme. Go visit soon.

ASHINGTON Olympia Health Club *204 Milburn Road, Ashington, Northumberland NE63. Tel: 01670 857430* Another good place with Power Chi classes. Fully equipped gym, sauna, sunbed and lounge area.

BEDLINGTON Paramount Health & Fitness *Glebe Road, Bedlington, Northumberland NE22. Tel: 01670 823223* Hatha Power Chi yoga plus a gym and sauna. Basic and OK place.

BERWICK-UPON-TWEED The Swan Centre For Leisure *Northumberland Road, Tweedmouth, Berwick-upon-Tweed, Northumberland TD15. Tel: 01289 330603* Body balance yoga plus pilates classes. Gym, pool, squash court, sauna, jacuzzi and steam room. Café. Try it out.

BLYTH Blyth Sports Centre *Bolam Avenue, Blyth, Northumberland NE24. Tel: 01670 352943* Yogalates plus general yoga. Exercise classes. Gym, pool, sauna and steam room. Café and bar.

CRAMLINGTON Better Bodies *High Pit Road, Cramlington, Northumberland NE23. Tel: 01670 590800* General yoga on offer plus a nice gym, exercise studio, toning table and sauna.

CRAMLINGTON Concordia Leisure Centre *Forum Way, Cramlington, Northumberland NE23. Tel: 01670 717423* Yoga once a week. Gym, swimming pool and sauna. Café and bar.

HEXHAM Wentworth Leisure Centre *Wentworth Park, Hexham, Northumberland NE46. Tel: 01434 607080* Nice facility. General yoga classes are offered plus a range of other activities for exercise and relaxation. Fitness studio and café.

MORPETH Morpeth Riverside Lesiure Centre *New Market, Morpeth, Northumberland NE61. Tel: 01670 514665*

Body balance yoga plus a pilates class. Nice pool, gym, plenty of other classes, sauna, steam room and beauty treatment room. Café and bar. Good place.

MORPETH Parklands Health Studio *New Market, Morpeth, Northumberland NE61. Tel: 01670 503975* General yoga classes and a gym, studio and other types of activity classes. Sunbed, sauna and beauty treatment room.

PRUDHOE The Buzz Factory *Swalwell Close, Prudhoe, Northumberland NE42. Tel: 01661 831002* This place has a women-only gym plus regular gym, sauna and café bar, along with regular classes. Nice buzz here.

YORKSHIRE

BARNSLEY Metrodome Leisure Complex *Queens Grounds, Queens Road, Barnsley, S. Yorkshire S70. Tel: 01226 730060 enquiries@bpl.org.com www.weblocal.co.uk/syorks/ leisure* Just off the M1 at Junction 37, this is a huge space full of activities and facilities – five swimming pools, ten badminton courts, food bar, crèche, sauna, steam room and restaurant to name just a few. The yoga classes are held in the Barnsley Premier Fitness Village facility.

CLEVELAND Cleveland Yoga & Well-Being Group *Tel: 01642 816055.* Contact Mavis Fielding

EASINGWOLD Crayke Yoga Club *Easingwold. Tel: 01347 23004* Contact Jane Cluley

HARROGATE Amanda Latchmore Yoga *York Place, Harrogate HG1. Tel: 01423 561173 amanda@harrogate yoga.com* Classes at several locations including The Hydro and The Friends Meeting House.

HUDDERSFIELD Charmony Yoga Circle *Huddersfield. Tel: 01484 535298* Contact June Morella

KIRKBY FLEETHAM Kirkby Fleetham Hall *Kirkby*

Fleetham, Northallerton, N. Yorkshire DL7. Tel: 01609 748747 A large and rather elegant English house devoted to the art of living in peace. The range of courses on offer covers yoga, regression therapy (or soul drama, as it is now called), the art of loving in peace, shiatsu, and neuro-linguistic programming. Open from March to October. Garden, guest lounge and TV. Vegetarian wholefood. Special diets catered for. Very quiet countryside. Access: train to Northallerton, which is eight miles away. Bus service limited.

MIDDLESBROUGH Numthorpe Yoga Group *Middlesbrough. Tel: 01642 817196* Contact Yvonne Muir

THIRSK Holy Rood House *10 Sowerby Road, Sowerby, Thirsk, N. Yorkshire YO7. Tel: 01845 522580 holyroodhouse@centrethirsk.fsnet.co.uk www.holyroodhouse.freeuk.com* A centre for health and pastoral care where you can find peace and relaxation with yoga. Holy Rood House is a gem of a place, nestling near the Hambleton hills. Courses on offer include pottery, drama, weaving and aromatherapy massage. Home-cooked food. A warm and friendly welcome.

YORK Anna Semlyen Yoga *York. Tel: 01904 654355 anna@yogainyork.co.uk www.semlyen.demon.co.uk/yoga/welcome.html* British Wheel of Yoga teacher who runs a large programme of classes each week in the York area. She teaches both Hatha and Astanga yoga, gives group as well as private lessons, and sometimes holds holiday yoga courses.

YORK Peter Finch Yoga *York. Tel: 01904 641732 pete@thefinches.demon.co.uk*

YORK Yoga for All *York. Tel: 01904 423340* Contact Jane Reed. Peter Finch and Jane Reed teach weekly classes. Contact either for details of current offerings.

WALES

GENERAL

Brecon Beacons Yoga Holidays *Cambridge Iyengar Yoga Centre, 59 Norfolk Terrace, Cambridge CB1 sashaperryman@ yahoo.com www.cambridgeyoga.co.uk/holiday/holiday.html* There are several yoga holiday retreats with Sasha Perryman in Penpont in the Brecon Beacons. The fourteen-bedroom house, owned by Gavin and Davina Hoog, is set in a magnificent area of natural beauty. The course includes two classes a day plus full board. Costs run at about £355. Contact Sasha Perryman and ask about her next yoga holiday programme.

Claire Senior Yoga *South Wales Area Clairesenior@ yahoo.com* Claire Senior (Kalavathia Devi) is a certified Rishi Culture Ashtanga yoga teacher, currently giving classes in and around South Wales.

ABERGAVENNY Clydach Village Hall *Clydach, Abergavenny, Gwent NP7. Tel: 01495 764233* Weekly class in general yoga.

BANGOR Life Foundation International Course Centre *Nant Ffrancon, Bethesda, Bangor, Gwynedd LL57. Tel: 01248 602900 enquiries@lifefoundation.org www.lifefoundation.org.uk* Situated in the beautiful Welsh mountains of Snowdonia National Park, this is the home base of the World Peace Flame, a peace initiative by peacemakers around the world. The team at the centre are from a wide range of backgrounds and they have come together to provide spiritual awareness, self-empowerment and self-development courses. Specialities include Dru yoga, meditation retreats and spiritual development courses. 'Tools for transformation' sums it up best. Open for retreats and course programme. No smoking. No alcohol. Spiritual help includes inner self-development, self-help tools, yoga and meditation. Everyone eats together. All meals are vegetarian.

CAERLEON Caerleon Comprehensive School *Coldbath Road, Caerleon, Newport, Gwent NP18. Tel: 01495 764233 www.yogauk.og* Regular weekly yoga class. All abilities welcomed.

CARDIFF Chapter Arts Centre *Market Road, Canton, Cardiff, South Glamorgan CF5. Tel: 01443 408065 kalavathi@ yoga-wales.co.uk www.yoga-wales.co.uk*

CARDIFF David Lloyd Leisure Centre *Cefn Coed, Cardiff, South Glamorgan CF48. Tel: 01685 384182 www. davidlloydleisure.co.uk* This is the number for the yoga teacher but you might like to check out this leisure club as it is part of a national chain with a high standard of facilities including gym and fitness suite.

CARDIFF Drop-In Yoga *Community Centre, Merthyr Tydfil, Cardiff, South Glamorgan CF48. Tel: 01685 384182* Hatha yoga including asana, pranayama, meditation and dynamic yoga.

CARDIFF Miskin Manor Health Club *Miskin, Cardiff, Mid Glamorgan CF72. Tel: 01443 225029 brittonjan@fsmail.net www.wellwithin.co.uk* The Miskin Manor Health Club is open to non-members for yoga and there are usually two sessions per week.

CARDIFF Yoga with Mary & Jason *30 Melrose Avenue, Cardiff, Wales CF1. Tel: 01222 482673*

CRICKHOWELL Arts Alive Centre *Old School, Brecon Road, Crickhowell, Powys NP8. Tel: 07960 167412 Oedw24@aol.com* Regular weekly yoga class, which includes chakras, yoga nidra and meditation.

HARLECH Support Group for Yoga Teachers & Students *Harlech. Tel: 01766 780365* Contact Margaret Ellis

LAMPETER Celian Millennium Hall *Cella, Near Lampeter,*

Cardiganshire SA48. Tel: 01570 422822 gro-mete@appleonline. net Twice-weekly classes for all ability levels.

LAMPETER University of Wales Lampeter *Catherine Stotts Room, Students Union, University of Wales Lampeter, College Street, Lampeter, Cardiganshire SA48. Tel: 01570 422822 gro-mete@appleonline.net* Weekly yoga class, sponsored by the Workers Educational Association. Free for students, low-income earners and state pensioners.

LLANDEILO Classical Yoga for the New Age *Llandeilo. Tel: 01348 831553* Contact Sue Armour

LLANDEILO Mandala Yoga Asram *Pantypistyll, Llansadwrn, Llandeilo, Carmarthenshire SA19. Tel: 01558 685358* Different programme of courses each year throughout the year. Both residential and day visitors are welcomed here.

LLANDEILO Padmasambhava *66 Rhosmaen Street, Llandeilo, Carmarthenshire SA19. Tel: 01558 823842*

LLANELLI Natural Healing Centre *Llanelli. Tel: 01554 757194* Contact Margaret Howells

PENARTH St Augustine's Church Hall *Albert Road, Penarth, South Glamorgan CF64. Tel: 029 207 08762* (Jacqueline Marshal – yoga teacher)

PONTYPOOL Little Mill Village Hall *Little Mill, Pontypool, Gwent NP15. www.yogauk.org* Weekly yoga class.

SWANSEA Govinda's *8 Craddock Street, Swansea, West Glamorgan SA1. Tel: 01792 526110 www.yogawales.co.uk*

SWANSEA Swansea University *Singleton, Swansea, West Glamorgan SA1. Tel: 01792 526110 www.yogawales.co.uk*

SWANSEA YMCA *1 The Kingsway, Swansea, West Glamorgan SA1. Tel: 01792 526110 www.yogawales.co.uk*

TREFFOREST Trefforest Community Centre *Kingsland Terrace, Trefforest, South Glamorgan. Tel: 01443 408065 kalavathi@yoga-wales.co.uk www.yoga-wales.co.uk*

USK Usk Primary School *Usk, Gwent NP15 www.yogauk.org*
WELSHPOOL Abhedashram *Camlad House, Forden, Welshpool, Powys SY21. Tel: 01938 580499* This Ashram and Residential Meditation and Conference Retreat Centre houses people who have committed their lives to the study and practice of a spiritual life in the methods of yoga and Vedanta traditions. Guidance is given in the practice of these two traditions. The Ashram has been established in Wales since 1983 under the auspices of the Universal Confluence of Yoga-Vedanta Luminary Trust. It welcomes people interested in this spiritual way of life in which there are two systems of Indian philosophy. In a new 1997 building, the centre is set in 29 acres of quiet countryside with regular day and weekend programmes. Open all year. Receives men and women. Centrally heated accommodation and plenty of rooms. Guest apartment. Increasing facilities here as refurbishment is an ongoing operation. Meals are vegetarian. Access: one hour from M6/M56 and less from the M54. Rail station ten minutes away.
WEST GLAMORGAN Loughor Welfare Hall *Woodlands Road, Loughor, West Glamorgan SA4. Tel: 01792 526110 helenamillar@aol.com www.yogawales.co.uk*

SCOTLAND

AYRSHIRE

LARGS Connections *48 Gallowgate Street, Largs, Ayrshire KA30. Tel: 01475 675533 manager@well-connected.biz www.well-connected.biz* Regular yoga classes are held throughout the week.

DUMFRIES & GALLOWAY

STRANRAER Johnny Glover Yoga *84 Eastwood Avenue, Stranraer DG9. Tel: 01776 704 994 yogafolk@aol.com*

DUNBARTONSHIRE

BEARSDEN Alexander Sports Centre *Milngavie Road, Bearsden, Glasgow G61. Tel: 0141 942 2233 pearlslane@ yahoo.com*

BEARSDEN Scout Hall *7 Rubislaw Drive, Bearsden, Glasgow G61. Tel: 0141 942 5814* You need to telephone to book yourself in here for the mixed-ability weekly yoga class.

BEARSDEN West of Scotland Yoga Teachers' Association *43 Roman Road, Bearsden, Glasgow G61. Tel: 0141 943 0597* Contact Pearl Slane

FIFE

Fife Yoga Group This group holds regular meetings through the winter months. For further information contact the secretary Jill Travers at *jill.travers@talk21.com*

GLASGOW

Allander Sports Centre *Milngavie Road, Glasgow G61. Tel: 01412 942 2233* Mixed-ability class.

Brahma Kumaris World Spiritual University *PO Box 4077, Crookston, Glasgow G53. Tel: 0141 883 3139 www.bkwsuscotland.com* Raja Yoga Meditation foundation course on offer here. All courses are free of charge.

Leisure Drome *147 Balmuildy Road, Bishopbriggs, Glasgow G64. Tel: 0141 772 6391* A weekly mixed-ability yoga class is on offer here.

GRAMPIAN

ABERDEEN Brahma Kumaris *66A Hamilton Place, Aberdeen, Grampian AB15. Tel: 01224 639105 aberdeen@bkwsu.com www.bkwsuscotland.com*

HIGHLANDS & ISLANDS

ALNESS New Yoga Class *The Perrins Centre, Alness, Highlands & Islands IV17. Tel: 01349 880682 sylvia.middleton2@btopenworld.com* A weekly mixed-ability yoga class suitable for all levels.

ISLE OF SKYE Quiraing Lodge *Staffin, Isle of Skye IV51. Tel: 01470 562330 www.quiraing-lodge.co.uk* The house is in a lovely setting, surrounded by an acre of garden sloping down to the shore, while behind rise the magnificent hills of the Quiraing. Good walks all around with bicycles available for those who want to explore further afield. The varied programme, which often includes a yoga retreat course, has an interest in deepening relationships with Gaia and the spiritual forces in nature as well as renewal of the Christian heritage and the experience of other faiths such as Buddhism. Events on offer range from Celtic Pilgrimage and Inner Silence to retreats to the Island of Iona celebrating the anniversaries of St Columba and St Augustine and their relevance to our lives today. Located almost at the top of Skye, the lodge is situated in an area of great earth power, ley lines, energy points and sacred sites. Many people come here to recover from life crises of health, work or relationships. Open from December to October. Facilities include a garden, library, guest lounge and telephone. Everyone eats together and the food is wholefood/vegetarian.

INVERCLYDE

GOUROCK Scottish Yoga Teachers' Association *16 Hilltop Crescent, Gourock, Inverclyde, Scotland PA19. Tel: 01475 633967 info@yogascotland.org.uk www.yogascotland.org.uk* Contact Joanna Reilly. The Scottish Yoga Teachers' Association (SYTA) was set up in 1988 after the dissolution of the Scottish Yoga Association, with the same purpose of promoting yoga in all its aspects throughout Scotland, to provide courses for the training of yoga teachers and seminars for anyone interested in yoga. Contact them for information on yoga classes and teachers in your area of Scotland. Membership is not just for teachers of yoga – it is open to all people who are interested in yoga. The Association is affiliated to the British Wheel of Yoga and the European Union of Federations of Yoga and has members around the world.

LOTHIAN

EDINBURGH Brahma Kumaris World Spiritual University *20 Polwarth Crescent, Edinburgh, Lothian EH11. Tel: 0131 2297220 mail@bkwsuedin.org.uk www.bkwsuscotland.com* Raja yoga meditation on regular offer.
EDINBURGH Edinburgh & Lothians Yoga Association (ELYA) *Tel: 0131 441 7214* Contact Lesley Hay for information on seminars, courses and other programmes including pranayama meditation.

EDINBURGH The Salisbury Centre 2 *Salisbury Road, Edinburgh EH16. Tel: 0131 667 5438 office@salisburycentre.org www.salisburycentre.org* The Salisbury Centre was founded in 1973 with the aim of establishing a centre in the city where people could find opportunities for spiritual and psychological growth. In a handsome Georgian house, set in organic gardens, the centre is a peaceful haven where classes run throughout the day, evening and over the weekend. There is a warm, homely feeling throughout the house, which has a bright, spacious first-level studio space, a pottery, smaller treatment/group rooms, a library overlooking the gardens and a kitchen where teas and coffees are available. Despite the busy programme, there is a real sense of peace and calm here. A small residential community live and work in the centre. There are weekly classes in meditation, yoga, t'ai chi, creative writing, pilates, pottery, stained glass, circle dancing, voice work. Weekend workshops vary but typically include astroshamanism, overtone singing, storytelling, healing and many other mind-body-spirit topics led by experienced national and international teachers.

MORAYSHIRE

FORRES Findhorn Foundation *The Universal Hall, The Park, Forres, Morayshire IV36. Tel: 01309 691170* For Yoga: *celia@diamondcoaching.com* For Findhorn Foundation Reception: *reception@findhorn.com* For Findhorn Foundation Accommodation: *accomms@findhorn.com www.findhorn.org* This is a well-publicised and famous place and can get very crowded in the summertime. The Community was founded in 1962 by three people, who believed in the principles that the source of life or God is accessible to each person and that nature, including earth, has intelligence and is part of a much greater plan. Nature spirits, or *devas*, are said to have allowed them to raise vegetables and exotic flowers from a barren soil of sand and gravel. Today Findhorn is a highly organised operation and one of the largest private communities in Britain, if not in the Western world. Enthusiasm, harmony and love are the precepts by which they all try to work and there is a strong emphasis on meditation. Courses of all descriptions, length and type, including yoga, run throughout the year. Such is the popularity of this place that accommodation usually needs to be booked months in advance. New Bold House, part of the Community, offers a live-work-meditate lifestyle for those who wish to share it. They have a separate programme and charges. There are also secondary island retreat centres, which are included in their brochure information. Open all year. The facilities range from houses, chalets, caravans and campsites plus a Visitors Centre and shopping. Children welcomed if supervised. Vegetarians catered for. There is a fixed price system and credit cards are accepted.

TAYSIDE

DUNDEE Yoga Association *Tayside, Lower Lesser Caird Hall, Dundee DD1. www.yogascotland.org.uk/index.html* The aim of the association is to support and encourage Tayside people to participate in the health-giving aspects of yoga and allied therapies. The contact is Jean Silvers, 23 Douglas Terrace, Broughty Ferry, Dundee, who teaches various day and half-day yoga seminars and courses.

IRELAND & NORTHERN IRELAND

GENERAL

Ashtanga Yoga In Ireland There are still few Ashtanga classes available in Northern Ireland, as this type of yoga needs devotion to practice for several years before taking a teaching certificate (while there are exceptions, students have usually practised Iyengar yoga before embarking on an Ashtanga course). The same applies to Iyengar yoga teachers. At present, there are some eleven qualified Iyengar teachers in Northern Ireland. Of the six who currently teach, two hold classes at Queen's Physical Education Centre Belfast (Marie Quail and Gloria Gilfillan).

Irish Yoga Association Contact Liam on *00353 86 8075379 info@irelandyoga.org*

Yoga Centre of Ireland *The Field of Doves, 10 Clanbrassil Road, Cultra, Ireland BT18. Tel: 028 9042 8370 norma.yoga@ btconnect.com*

Yoga Fellowship of Northern Ireland *19 Elsmere Park, Belfast BT5. Tel: 028 9070 5913 www.yfni.co.uk info@ynfi.co.uk*

Yoga Therapy and Training Centre *16 Kinghill Road, Cabra, Nr Rathfriland Newry, County Down BT34. Tel: 028 4063 0686 info@yogateachers.net* One of the foremost teaching and training centres for yoga, yoga therapy and related subjects in Northern Ireland. Arranged in a domestic setting of a house and garden surrounded by tall hedges, it is about 40 miles from Belfast and 65 miles from Dublin. The centre comprises a large yoga practice room with stay-over ensuite facilities, coffee area, car park and gardens. There are views of the Mourne Mountains and the situation is peaceful for meditation. A ten-week course for beginners is available. Workshops are given by Marie Quail and others such as Ruth White, Shiv Sharma, Sophy Hoare and, for those wishing to follow the Ashtanga yoga path, Orla Punch and Neil Kelleher. Veggie cuisine.

ANTRIM

BELFAST Cecilia Gilbert *11 Marylebone Park, Belfast BT9. Tel: 028 9066 1334*

BELFAST Deirdre Heaney *31 Breda Park, Belfast. Tel: 028 9080 8553*

BELFAST Gill Henderson *6 Beechmount Park, Upper Lisburn Road, Belfast BT10. Tel: 07879 810630*

BELFAST Valerie McCrory *13 Wynchurch Avenue, Belfast,BT6. Tel: 028 9079 5472*

BELFAST Yoga Therapy and Training Centre Lots of classes and courses on offer. Workshops given by Marie Quail. You need to check out their website to get details on what is on offer and where. Very popular and often books up quickly.

CARRICKFERGUS Colleen Thompson *21 Marine Parade, Whitehead, Carrickfergus, Antrim BT38. Tel: 028 9335 3499*

LARNE Drumalis Retreat Centre *Glenarm Road, Larne, Antrim BT40. Tel: 028 2827 2196 dspace.dial.pipex.com/ drumalis* The Drumalis Vision Statement says it all: *Drumalis is a place of welcome, an oasis on the journey of life. A living community where all experience the power of God's love and compassion. Discover and value their gifts. Seek to be healers in a divided world. Grow in their relationship with God and all Creation. We draw our life and strength from sharing and prayer.* The house itself is a rambling late Victorian mansion with an awe-inspiring view across Larne Harbour. The programme here includes: Healing Touch Workshop, Yoga, Prayer &

Painting, Dream Retreat, Transformation Retreat. Open all year except Christmas and Easter. Non-retreaters in self-catering cottages only. Facilities include garden, library and guest lounge. Everyone eats together – traditional food. Vegetarians and special diets are catered for. Access: from Belfast take M2, leave at exit A8. By train, bus and harbour follow signs for the Coast Road. Drumalis is on right before Bankhands Lane just before leaving the town.

BALLYMENA

Claire O'Neill *9 Farmlodge Avenue, Ballymena BT43. Tel: 028 2564 7091*

CORK

An Sanctoir *Bawnaknockane Ballydehob, West Cork. Tel: 028 37155 www.westcorkweb.ie/ansanctoir sanctoir@eircom.net*

DERRY

Maggie McKinney *7 Taylor's Row, Coleraine, Derry. Tel: 028 7032 6986*
Majella McIntyre *28 Tamneymore Park, Waterside, Derry BT47. Tel: 028 7131 3158/07813 849 215*

DOWN

Emmet Devlin *23 Cairnhill, Newry, Down BT34. Tel: 028 3026 4865 emmetdevlin@ireland.com* Dr Devlin is a consultant physician at Daisy Hill Hospital and a yoga therapist.
Barbara Gibson *93 Church Street, Newtownards, Down BT23. Tel: 028 9182 6553 pilates@btclick.com*
Eddie Kelly *20 Dora Avenue, Newry, Down. Tel: 028 3026 8769*
Sian Maxwell *Old Court Farm, Stratford, Downpatrick, Down*

BT30. Tel: 028 4488 1318

Siobhan McQuade *30 Glenveigh, Chancellors Road, Newry, Down BT35. Tel: 028 3025 1690* siobhanmcquade@ hotmail.com

Jane Tucker *52 Kenlis Street, Banbridge, Down BT32. Tel: 0781 826 2159*

Lisa Wells *13 Ardkeel Park, Newcastle, Down BT33. Tel: 028 4372 4907* lisaisa@ukonline.co.uk

DUBLIN

Deirdre O'Rourke *16 Abbey Court, Abbey Road, Monkstown, Dublin. Tel: 00353 864000851* deeyoga@yahoo.com

Paula Flood *15 Dalcassian Downs, Glasnevin, Dublin 11. Tel: 00353 1860 1110*

Susan Church *Dublin. Tel: 00353 8762 10402* www.susan churchyogacentral.com

Viniyoga Ireland *Dublin. Tel: 00353 1288 9012* hannegil lespie@eircom.net Contact Hanna Gillespie

FERMANAGH

Gabriele Tottenham *Ininsh Beg Cottages, Innish Beg, Blaney, Enniskillen, Fermanagh BT93. Tel: 00353 6864 1525*

GALWAY

Burren Yoga Meditation Centre *Lig do Scith, Cappaghmore, Kinvara, Galway, Ireland. Tel: 353 091 637 680* burrenyoga@ yahoo.com www.burrenyoga.com This is a special yoga retreat centre where Ashtanga and Iyengar yoga are offered plus Satyananda yoga, pilates and fitness courses and retreats. The centre is about 50 minutes by car from Shannon Airport. There is an exciting year-round programme of various courses and retreats with different teachers.

KERRY

DINGLE Ilonka Miklosi *Green St, Baile na Buaile, Dingle, Kerry. Tel: 00353 6691 51765*

INCH Lios Dana *The Natural Living Centre, Inch, Annascaul, Kerry. Tel: 066 915 8189 www.holistic.ie/liosdana* Claiming to be Ireland's leading holistic holiday centre for rest and renewal and the practice of a new approach to life, Lios Dana is set in a wonderful location on the southern shoreline of the Dingle peninsula in the south-west of Ireland. There are three-day programmes, which include yoga and shiatsu massage, group courses from March to October in a variety of holist disciplines, or you can come for a simple holiday break and use the centre's facilities. Country walks, sea and mountains and early Christian sites all here. Open all year. Eight bedrooms. Self-catering chalets. Large exercise room, library, guest lounge, conservatories, hot and cool pool. Creative and healing exercises and therapies. Meals are vegetarian. Access: rail – to Tralee and then bus. Car: 2 hours from Cork or Limerick. Air: 20 miles from Kerry County airport.

LOUTH

Carmel McArdle *Cappocksgreen, Ardee, Louth. Tel: 00353 4168 53445*

MAYO

Lucy Bingham McAndrew *Binghamstown, Ballina, Mayo. Tel: 00353 9781205 loosie@eircom.net*

MEATH

Rose Marie Murphy *Demailstown, Wilkinstown, Navan, Meath. Tel: 00353 4654362*

WICKLOW

Rani Sheilagh Dunn *County Wicklow. Tel: 00353 4586 7202*
info@prana.ie. www.prana.ie

YOGA HOLIDAY RETREATS

AUSTRALIA

Australia has a number of serious yoga centres. To get a complete picture you need to visit the Australian yoga website (www.ayl.com), where you will find an impressive list of current yoga retreat programmes. Here are a few to get you thinking about combining a holiday in Australia with yoga and fitness.

MELBOURNE The Fitzroy Astanga Yoga School *Russia House, Corner of Greeves & Gore Street, Fitzroy, Melbourne.* Astanga yoga in a serious teaching situation. Write to them to find out how you might combine a holiday and a course in Atanga.

SYDNEY Gladesville Yoga Association *Sydney www. spiritofyoga.com* Swamis Shabdavani and Priyaratna run classes at their Gladesville Ashram in Sydney. The Gladesville Yoga Association is a non-profit-making organisation of yoga teachers and students dedicated to serving society by preserving and living the principles of yoga through community, selfless service, support, communication and education.

WOLLONGONG Satyam Yoga Centre Centre *www.satyamyoga.com* Satyam Yoga Centre conducts classes in the Wollongong area and is under the directorship of Swamis Mounomurti Saraswati and Sannyasi Mantrabindu. This centre has a huge library of research papers from the Swami Vivekananda Yoga Anusandhana Samsthana (Research Foundation) in India.

CRETE

Yoga Plus *177 Ditchling Road, Brighton, East Sussex BN1. Tel:*

01273 276175 yogaplus@pavilion.co.uk www.yogaplus.co.uk Crete is one of the largest of the Greek islands, full of sunshine, beauty and peace and loaded with history. Life moves slowly here – which sounds about right for a yoga holiday. Founded some ten years ago in a small bay in southern Crete, Yoga Plus is well organised and enables you to discover and practise yoga, rest, relax and get a revitalisation of mind and spirit. There is a full schedule of sessions of Astanga Vinyasa yoga along with other forms of yoga practice. In addition there is a full programme of courses such as t'ai chi, Chi Kung, holistic massage, collage and papermaking, adventure walks, Alexander technique, Voiceworks, pilates, swimming, Cretan history, and even Salsa and Latin dancing. A popular and busy place where the teaching style is to guide and encourage students to discover their full potential and not put any pressure on them. Yoga Plus is now one of Europe's foremost places for a holiday with special purpose.

Egypt

West London Yogashala *Basement, 22 Cleveland Terrace, Bayswater, London W2. Tel: 020 7402 2217 yogashala@ btinternet.com www.yogashala.co.uk* Shadow yoga – or as it is often called, Cutting-Edge Hatha yoga – is relatively new to Britain and there are so far only two people qualified to teach it in the country. One of these is William Robertson, a nurse and counsellor, who trained with Shandor Remete in Australia and brought the Shadow style of Hatha yoga to London, setting up a small practice studio in Bayswater. With roots in Iyengar and Astanga Vinyasa yoga, Shadow yoga integrates asanas, breathing and martial arts. This dynamic approach is especially effective in developing resilience, independence, vitality and physical strength. Individual instruction is offered to every student, who is encouraged to practise independently in the warm and welcoming studio. There are also small group classes held on a regular basis for both beginners and the more experienced. Martial Qigong as well as Qigong for medical therapy is offered in weekly classes as well. Shadow yoga retreats are held in Egypt and Thailand on a regular basis.

FRANCE

Alternative spirituality facilities and programmes have increased dramatically in France, with a great expansion of courses, workshops, training and retreats. A quick look in any French magazine shop will confirm the wide range of interests the French have in holistic and alternative spirituality and health approaches, including wide enthusiasm for yoga. These centres and their programmes are often exciting, enabling and positive in terms of destressing, exploration of new horizons, self-improvement and discovering the inner person. Yoga is taught all over France and almost as popular is t'ai chi, circle and African dancing, and other forms of mind-body-spirit endeavours.

La Fédération Nationale des Enseignants de Yoga (F.N.E.Y.), Yse Masquelier, 3 Rue Aubriot, F-75004 Paris. Tel: 01427 00305

Centre Atma 50 Rue des Lices, 8400 Avignon. Tel: 04902 73514

Centre de Yoga Iyengar de Lyon Clos de Fourviere II, 40 Rue Roger Radisson, 69005 Lyon. Tel: 04783 60384

Editions Terre du Ciel BP 2050, 13 Rue Henri IV, 69227 Lyon. Tel: 0472 410751 The Terre du Ciel is one of the best sources in France for information about aspects of Christian, Judaic, Buddhist and Sufi spirituality, yoga, holistic health methods, and many of the leading as well as the somewhat obscure mind-body-spirit approaches to self-awareness and harmony with others and with planet earth. The aim of Terre du Ciel is to create and bring together invitations for change and renewal of self. They publish a bi-monthly journal with articles and listings of workshops and courses which reflect this aim.

Ecole Francaise de Yoga du Sud-Est *18 Rue Victor Leydet, 13100 Aix-en-Provence. Tel: 04422 79220*

Fédération Inter-Régionale de Hatha-Yoga *322 Rue Saint Honoré, 75001 Paris. Tel: 04426 03210*

Kaivalyadhama-France *Lozeron, 26400 Gigors-et-Lozeron. Tel: 04757 64295*

L'Association Provencale de Hatha Yoga *12 Rue J. Daret, Aix-en-Provence. Tel: 05426 41854*

La Fédération Tantra Kundalini Yoga *Chateau Laroque, 33890 Juillas*

La Fédération des Yogas Traditionnels *Andr´Riehl, 65 Rue des Cedres, 84120 Pertuis. Tel: 04900 96527*

La Val Dieu *Pyrenees. Tel: 01225 311826* Contact Annette Tolson

La Yoga Thérapie *Christine Campagnac-Morette, 5 Place du Général Beuret, 75015 Paris*

AIN Bourg en Brese *Auris, 6 Rue Viala, 01000 Bourg en Bresse, Ain. Tel: 0474 224886* Alternative spirituality. Yoga, destressing, meditation, chanting, voice workshops and personal therapies are all on offer here. Send for brochure.

AVIGNON Centre Atma *50 Rue des Liuces, 84000 Avignon. Tel: 0490 273514* Alternative spirituality. The centre is open all year for courses and workshops in yoga and massage. They also organise a group expedition to India each year. Write for brochure.

CREUSE La Cellette *Le Blé en Herbe* (The Ripening Seed), *Puissetier, 23350 La Cellette, Creuse. Tel: 0555 806283*

Alternative spirituality – eco-spirituality. Holistic retreats. Open from March to November. Receives men, women, children, groups. Set in the rolling foothills of the Massif Central, this well-established place has an eight-acre organic garden with wild flower fields and is surrounded by unspoiled countryside. The lifestyle here is one of simplicity and closeness to nature. A variety of options for a get-away-from-it-all retreat are on offer, including Holistic Massage, African Dancing, Meditation of Dance, Shiatsu & Healing, Sacred Space for Women and Herbal Medicine. Personal talks and group sharing. Two single rooms, four double rooms, camping and caravan site, a barn. Vegetarian food. Costs about 170 francs per day full board, camping 25 francs a night. Highly recommended.

DORDOGNE St Crépin Carlucet *Centre Eviel Les Granges, 24590 St Crépin Carlucet. Tel: 0553 289327* Alternative spirituality. This is a centre for personal development and awakening the spiritual in you. Courses on offer may include workshops with titles like Opening The Heart, The Inner Clown, Truth Through Painting, Intuitive Massage, Relaxation Techniques and Bio-Dance. Send for information on current year's programme and rates.

DROME Saint-Bonnet de Valclérieux *Chateau de Valclérieux, Saint-Bonnet de Valclérieux, 26350 Crépol, Drome. Tel: 0475 717067* Alternative spirituality. A beautiful and popular place for yoga and various health therapy courses and workshops for both individuals and groups. Send for information and charges on year's current programme.

LASLADES La Seve *40 Route de Tarbes, 653560 Laslades. Tel: 0562 350834* Mind, body, spirit. A programme of healing courses and experience of self, including discovering your relationship in the zodiac signs, essential oil therapies, and rediscovery of the senses of taste, sight, hearing, touching and smell.

LOIRET Château du Yoga Sivananda *Neuville au Bois, Loiret, Orléans 45000 www.sivananda.org/orleans/indeng.htm* The Château du Yoga Sivananda is one of the International Sivananda Yoga Vedanta centres whose aim is to spread ancient teachings of yoga to all. This place, formally an ashram, is located about 100 kilometres south of Paris and very close to the city of Orléans. It is a large property in a calm and peaceful setting near one of France's largest forests. Activities take place throughout the year. As well as the normal daily timetable, into which you can book yourself, there are special programmes and retreats. Some examples of recent ones include Karma Yoga Weekend; Nana Yoga – inner awakening through the power of sacred sounds with live music; Yoga and Hiking; Yoga and Stress Management; Fasting Weekend; Yoga, Sport and Nature; Yoga and the Family; Festival of Yoga and the Sacred Arts.

LOT La Buissiére *Lot Valley www.yogafrance.com* Yoga and walking in rural France, staying in a comfortable house with two acres of private parkland and pool.

LOZERE The Sun Centre *Prades, 48160 St Martin de Boubaux. Tel: 0033 4 66 45 59 63 www.thesuncentre.net* A yoga and Ayurveda therapy centre recently set up and opened by Alex Duncan and his wife Sharon. Morning yoga on a large outdoor deck in the woods in a beautiful setting. The food is organic vegetarian and cooked according to Ayurvedic principles. The accommodation is simple but comfortable in twin-bedded rooms. 'Uncluttered comfort' is how one guest described it. The Sun Centre is located halfway up a mountain overlooking a deserted valley – quiet, unspoiled, very green, with lots of woodland walks. Sounds just like a place the famous spirituality writer Thomas Merton, who was born at nearby Prades, would have liked. Comments from guests are full of praise for this place: 'I came away refreshed, revitalised and rested.' 'Had a wonderful stay.' 'Alex's knowledge of his subject was faultless.' 'First-rate teaching.' 'Great food!' 'Very good value for money.' 'All in all, very spiritually uplifting.' With afternoons largely free, additional activities include walking, river swimming or sunbathing in the gardens, and every other night there's some kind of evening activity – star gazing, chanting, even group foot massage. The cost runs at about £285 plus getting there. Pick-up possible from Nimes airport, about two hours away by car.

MAUREILLAS Féderation Internationale de Yoga Himalayen c/o Stephane-Jean, Les Ilipotiers, Las Illas Village, 66480 Maureillas. Tel: 0033 06 11 51 47 53; 0033 04 68 83 04 76 www.membres.lycos.fr/himalaya/program Hatha yoga programmes including yoga, Ayurveda and psychotherapy workshops. Suitable for both beginners and advanced practitioners. Diet and personal schedule with individual instruction. Location for workshops varies but has been in the beautiful Luberon area in Provence with local accommodation at a good hotel. Price, at around €500, includes workshop, meals and accommodation.

MONTCUQ Le Chartrou Belmonet, 46800 Montcuq. Tel: 0565 319023 Alternative spirituality. A naturopathy retreat for destressing and increasing your energies by means of diet, nutrition and revitalisation, which maximise the natural biological forces of your body. Brochure with events and courses plus charges available. If treatments are on offer always make certain you understand how much is being charged for what.

PARIS Centre International Sivanda de Yoga Vedanta 123 Boulevard de Sébastopol, 75002 Paris. Tel: 01 40 26 77 49

With centres and ashrams around the world, this organisation has trained over 8,000 yoga teachers. Send for information on courses and study available in France. The centres were founded by Swami Vishnudevananda and are run as a non-profit-making organisation whose purpose is to propagate the teachings of yoga and Vedanta as a means of achieving physical, mental and spiritual wellbeing and self-realisation.

PRADES Star of Light Mountain Retreat Centre *Maison Bird, Conat, 66500 Prades. Tel: 04 68960480 bird.conat@ easynet.fr* Mind, body, spirit. Course and workshop programmes including Hatha yoga, Reiki healing, and workshops with titles such as Men, Stress, Health & Wellbeing and The Zodiac Of Your Soul. Charges run from £100 per person for the course plus shared accommodation at £210 per person per week.

TOULOUSE Scandinavian Yoga & Meditation School *46 Rue de Metz, 31000 Toulouse. Tel: +33 561 251 769*

GREECE

MANI Yoga Practice *Tel: 020 7928 7527 www.yogapractice.net* Courses are taught by Kristina Karitinos and Michael Anastassiades in the Greek coastal region of Mani. The rooms are simple but overlook the sea, and there are yoga lessons every morning for two hours. The rest of the day is free to swim and explore the local fishing village of Limeni and historic Itylos. Check out the write-up in the *Telegraph Magazine* for the week of 25 January 2003. Current prices are about £450 a week.

PAROS Yoga Workshop *Aliki, Paros, Greece. Tel: +30 22840 92042 shakti@yoga-paros.com www.yoga-paros.com* Paros is one of the most central of the Cycladic Islands. The eight-day yoga workshop is held in a yoga studio in a small fishing village with lovely beaches. There are restaurants and small ferry boats to take you to other islands for day visits. The two teachers at this time are Jeanner Buntix, a qualified yoga teacher and body-orientated psychotherapist who trained in India under B. K. S. Iyengar, and Oona Giesen, who has some 30 years yoga training under her belt and teaches in both Amsterdam and Paros. Classes are usually in the mornings, and then you are free to relax and enjoy this beautiful Greek island and its people.

SKYROS Skyros Holistic Holidays *92 Prince of Wales Road, London NW5. Tel: 020 7267 4424/020 7284 3065 enquiries@ sykros greece@skyros.com www.skyros.com* Skyros has built an enviable reputation for providing a happy, unforgettable holiday experience on this famous island. 'New friends', 'new horizons' and 'renewal of body and mind' are all expressions of how people feel about their adventure. 'Magical' seems to sum it up best. The creative self is emphasised on the courses here. A typical day may start with yoga or a swim in the warm sea and end with dinner after a day of activities and relaxation. There are many courses on offer including, of course, yoga taught by qualified teachers.

India

GOA Purple Valley Yoga Centre *Northern Goa, India. Tel: (0091) (0) 98 23 099 788* (Annie Gurton) *www.yogagoa.com* Situated in northern Goa on the west coast of India, the centre has two locations. One is a drop-in place that holds classes six days a week. These are held at the Hotel Bougainvillea, a Goan country house with swimming pool. About 24 to a class for Ashtanga yoga. The other place, the Purple Valley Retreat, is under construction about 3 kilometres away. Here there will be a purpose-built shala for

40 students, situated in a little valley among palm and banana trees. There is to be a twelve-room house and an annexe with further rooms. Sounds a delightful yoga retreat in the country where it all started – but check out what stage the construction is at and exactly what is on offer in terms of facilities before you book. Goa is madly popular and a favourite drop-out place for Western Europeans. Beaches, nightlife and clubbing, easy living, the warmth of the people, good food and cheap accommodation continue to hold their appeal.

ITALY

CASPERIA Sunflower Retreats *The Manor House, Kings Norton, Leicestershire LE7. Tel: 0116 2599422 Casperia, Italy: Tel: 0039 0765 639015 Mobile: 0039 339 7043595 www.sunflowerretreats.com* Casperia is a hilltop village in the heart of the Sabina Mountains, about one and a half hours from Rome. It is a place of great natural beauty surrounded by olive groves, vineyards and mountains – all the things, plus delicious local food, that make us long for Italy. The yoga holidays and retreats here are run either on the basis of a group class or one-to-one tuition. The yoga is suitable for beginners as well as the more experienced yoga practitioner. The teaching is done by Lucy Bremner, an internationally qualified Fryog yoga teacher who has studied yoga in the UK, India, Nepal and Italy over the past fourteen years. Sunflower also has other qualified guest yoga teachers from around the world. The yoga classes include physical movements, breathing, meditation and relaxation. The programme for the coming year is available either on their website, as above, or by contacting them direct in either Italy or Britain. Travel is easy with airports not too far away and trains from Rome to

Casperia with final local transportation arrangements possible.

TUSCANY Yoga in Tuscany *Ebbio Villa, Monteriggioni, Tuscany, Italy www.globalyogajourneys.com* Ebbio Villa is a working organic farm situated in the heart of popular and beautiful Tuscany. Evergreen forest surrounds the farm and yet it is only some 11 kilometres from Siena and 42 kilometres from Florence. Climate plays an important part of an activity holiday – May and September are the ideal months. The welcome at Ebbio Villa is warm and charming. There is a barn converted into a yoga studio. The teachers here are Sudhakar Ken McRae and Kathleen Knipp, who have many years of yoga teaching experience and are very well known in America, where they have their main yoga teaching base. The yoga practice used on the retreats here is Kripalu yoga, which places less emphasis on physical practice and more on developing new ways of awareness and being, taking the person into living fully in the present moment. In addition to the yoga retreats in Tuscany, these teachers also hold retreats in the Costa Rica mountains and rainforest.

UMBRIA Venture Out *575 Pierce Street, San Francisco, CA 94117, USA www.venture-out.com/yoga.htm* Venture Out is a travel agency specialising in small carefully fashioned group tours in Italy and other places for gay and lesbian holidaymakers. For example, a current tour, Yoga & Medieval Hilltowns of Central Italy, offers regular yoga practice with a qualified teacher, Arthus Scappaticci, who draws on Iyengar and Ashtanga yoga techniques for his teaching. He is from San Francisco, where he conducts private and public yoga classes. The accommodation for this tour is in charming Italian farms, like hotels but with a relaxed and welcoming atmosphere. There are excursions to nearby towns like Spoleto, Assisi and Perugia.

LANZAROTE

Holistic Holidays *Villa Isis, Los Topes, 35572 Tias, Lanzarote, Canary Islands. Tel: 0034 928 524 216 UK Brochure Line: 020 7692 0633 enquiries@hoho.co.uk www.hoho.co.uk* A well-organised and very professionally run holiday centre for yoga and other healing arts such as shiatsu and reiki. All-year-round summer-type climate plus vegetarian cuisine, unspoiled beaches and a swimming pool at the villa provide a wonderful opportunity for a relaxing yoga holiday. The yoga director, Lynne Oliver, is a dedicated teacher and her words on yoga in the brochure give a good idea of her approach to yoga practice. Those who have been here on holiday speak of it in glowing terms, some feeling the experience brought them a new vision of themselves and their life.

SCANDINAVIA

Yoga is practised throughout the Scandinavian countries and there are many schools running summer retreats and courses. The climate can be hot and delightful in mid-summer with many sporting activities also available including lots of sailing and messing around with boats.

DENMARK Scandinavian Yoga & Meditation School *Kobmagergade 65, DK-1150 Copenhagen. Tel: +45 33 14 11 40*

DENMARK Scandinavian Yoga & Meditation School *Vestergade 45, DK-8000, Arhus. Tel: +45 86 19 40 33*

DENMARK Scandinavian Yoga & Meditation School *Kongensgade 12B, DK-3000, Elsinore. Tel: +45 49 21 20 68*

FINLAND Scandinavian Yoga & Meditation School *Sukula, 30100 Forssa. Tel: +358 16 4350499*

NORWAY Scandinavian Yoga & Meditation School *Georgenes Verft 3, N-5011, Bergen. Tel: +47 56 14 33 10*

NORWAY The Yoga Center *Stavanger, Norway* The Norwegian yoga teacher Christian Paaske has a large yoga school in Norway and is warmly regarded by those he teaches. Paaske also writes articles about yoga and related subjects and these can be downloaded.

SWEDEN Scandinavian Yoga & Meditation School *Haa Course Centre, S-34013 Hammeda, Sweden. Tel: +46 372 550 63 www.sacand-yoga.org* The Danish yogi Swami Janakananda founded this organisation for yoga in 1970 in Copenhagen. It consists of a group of teachers who run several independent schools in Scandinavia and also in Germany. Tantric yoga and meditation methods are taught and there are retreats at the Haa International Course Centre in southern Sweden. These include a three-month Sadhana course, Kriya yoga, Shakti and Nidra yoga, and a programme of ten- to fourteen-day courses. Most are taught in English but sometimes German is available. All retreats, courses and lectures aim at increasing awareness and experience of body, mind, energy and consciousness. For relaxing, there are walks, and horse riding is available in the countryside venues. The group is recognised by the International Yoga Federation.

SPAIN

In recent years, there has been a big increase in the number of alternative spirituality and holistic health centres in Spain. The warm weather and relaxed atmosphere provides restful settings for many healing and renewal programmes including destressing courses, yoga, relaxation techniques, complementary health methods and development of new inner values for self-realisation. Often set in sunny holiday sites like Granada, the core aim is to get you to relax and be renewed in a holistic approach. There are more and more yoga retreats held in Spain by British yoga teachers. These are often not established programmes but arranged on a year-by-year basis. Information on an actual programme can quickly go out of date so it's best to decide on Spain as your yoga holiday destination, discuss it with your local yoga teacher and then surf the net. In addition to the information at the end of this book, you might like to try the following websites and search names:

www.yogaholidays.net
www.bodyworkposters.com/yogalinks.html
www.holistic-online.com
www.yogadirectory.com/retreats_andvacations
Ashtanga Yoga and Ayurveda Retreats in South Spain
Ashtanga Yoga and Ayurvedic Retreats in Ibiza

GENERAL
Duncan Hulin Holistic Yoga *Duncan@devonyoga.com* *www.devonyoga.com* Duncan Hulin, who holds regular yoga classes in Exeter and Sidmouth, also organises yoga holidays in southern Spain (and Kerala, south India). There are a number of other yoga retreats and events on offer in his programmes.

YogaSpace *Basement Studio, 35/37 Thomas Street, Manchester M4. Tel: 0161 288 6918 www.yogaspace.org.uk* Yoga retreats are planned for a residential centre in Spain so get in touch to find out the programme. Founded in 2001, YogaSpace is relatively new and the first in central Manchester. Evening and day classes and courses in many styles of yoga are on offer there. All teachers are accredited and the director of the studio invites only those teachers who have a strong understanding of the spiritual dimension of yoga as well as a high proficiency in the physical postures and movements. It is expected that this standard will be used for any yoga courses held abroad.

DIEGO DE LEON Sivananda Yoga Vedanta Centre *Clerao 4, Diego de Leon. Tel: 91 361 5150* Part of the international Sivananda Yoga Vedanta Centres in France. Yoga courses, teachings and workshops.

GRANADA Cortijo Romero *18400 Órgiva, Granada. Tel: 0034 958 784 252 Information & Bookings: 01494 782720 UK address: Little Grove, Grove Lane, Chesham, HP5* Cortijo Romero has been established for some years now and is located in an inspiring location in a wonderful climate. The courses are designed for personal rest and renewal and the enrichment and discovery of self. Examples of what is offered are: Movement & Stillness for learning to be grounded in who you are, Yoga for Form & Feeling, and Forgiveness, Gratitude & Grace for dealing with issues of human development. Facilities include swimming pool, orchard, three single rooms, eleven doubles, guest lounge and telephone. Personal talks, group sharing, meditation and directed study all take place.

IBIZA El Jardin de Luz *Apdo 1126, 07800 Ibiza. Tel: 0034 971 334 644* Alternative spirituality. Open June to October. A spacious place without much luxury but lots of beauty with the emphasis on creativity and simplicity. Accommodation for 34 in dormitories. Meals are taken together. Food is international cuisine and vegetarians are catered for. Nice garden. Set in a forest about 2 kilometres from the beach.

IBIZA Windfire Yoga Retreat *36 Stanbridge Road, London SW15. Tel: 020 8780 3050*

IZNATE Maggie Levien *Calle Malaga 41, Iznate 29792. Tel: 0034 952 509603/0034 630 718204* Home of yoga teacher Maggie Levien, who teaches beginners in one-to-one sessions while staying on holiday in her self-contained apartment in a traditional old house in a white-washed Spanish village. She helps you discover what is suitable for you in yoga practice and caters for any physical limitations for the different yoga move-ments. Beautiful views, lovely walks, close to mountains and a nature reserve, and only about twenty minutes from the coast.

MALAGA Montana Palmera *Alta Axarquia, Malaga, Spain. Tel: 0034 952 536 506 (Both Spanish & English are spoken) montpalmera@hotmail.com www.andalucia.co.uk/montana_palmera* Montana Palmera is a purpose-built mountain retreat about an hour from Malaga with its own swimming pool and nine en-suite bedrooms. A garden and terrace and nearby horse riding, walking, sailing and tennis complete the picture. There are a number of yoga retreats usually on offer in a good programme including Iyengar yoga, Kundalini yoga and Sivananda yoga. The price, which varies according to season, includes full board with two hours' instruction each day for five days of your week's stay here.

MAJORCA Yoga & Meditation Seminars *Majorca* Contact Derwina Newell, *125 High St, Hadleigh, Suffolk IP7 Tel: 01473 822761*

OVIEDO Centro de Ashtanga Yoga *C/ San Bernabé No. 7, 30, 33002 Oviedo, Asturias. Tel: 0034 985226574 astanga@mx3.redestb.es* Thomás Zorzo Diez is a certified teacher and he works with Camino Diez Vinuela.

ZARAGOZA Associacion Espangnola de Praticantes de Yoga *10 Casa Jimenes, 50004 Zaragoza. Tel: 97621 956016* Contact Mrs Manuel Morata

THAILAND

West London Yogashala *Basement, 22 Cleveland Terrace, Bayswater, London W2. Tel: 020 7402 2217 yogashala@btinternet.com www.yogashala.co.uk* See entry for Egypt above. Shadow yoga retreats are held in Thailand on a regular basis.

TUNISIA

Jasmine Journeys *Sunnyway Tunisian Holidays, Tunisia House, 53 London Street, Southport PR9. Tel: 0845 130 7999 Tel: Tunisia: 00216 72 278 665 christinahatt@care2.com res@ sunnyway-tunisia.co.uk www.sunnyway-tunisia.co.uk* Jasmine Journeys runs yoga holidays with teacher Christina Hatt with classes suitable for all levels from beginners to advanced. Daily yoga workshops are designed to increase your flexibility, improve your circulation, and reduce tension in your body. Tunisia is a marvellous holiday destination with clean air, sunshine and blue skies. Lots of other activities can be arranged from horse riding and scuba diving to paragliding and golf. In addition to yoga you can also enrol for belly dancing, which will bring you a new and exciting expression of the inner self.

UNITED STATES

From California to Maine, America offers yoga classes, courses, centres and retreats. Yoga is taken seriously and many teachers have been students under yoga masters abroad, especially in India. Here is just one yoga retreat holiday that appealed to us:

Sedona Spirit Yoga *Arizona, USA. Tel: 928 282 9592 www.sedonaspirityoga.com* Sedona offers various yoga and activity and healing retreats. These include spirit yoga and hiking retreats, Phoenix Rising yoga sessions, yoga hikes in the Red Rocks area of Arizona, and transformational yoga retreats. These are in Sedona, Arizona, but retreats are also organised in Costa Rica, which has become a very popular holiday destination for Americans. The Costa Rican retreats are held at a lovely place, the Pura Vida Retreat Spa, which has a yoga studio with inspiring views. Maheshvari (Johanna Mosca, PhD), who leads the courses, is the author of *YogaLife: 10 Steps to Freedom* and a certified Kripalu yoga instructor, bodyworker and Phoenix Rising yoga therapist. She has been teaching yoga for over thirteen years. Sedona Spirit yoga is based on the gentle Kripalu yoga of self-acceptance, and includes a variety of styles and partner poses, plus toning, chakra balancing and playfulness. Maheshvari has studied extensively with Rama Jyoti, a world authority, and served on the founding board of the American Yoga College.

HELPFUL PUBLICATIONS

While some of these magazines may contain articles related to yoga and yoga practice, it is the advertisements for workshops and courses that make them useful. *Spectrum*, Journal of the British Wheel of Yoga, is the most helpful of all these publications as its direct aim is to provide information on yoga classes and contacts.

Spectrum Journal of the British Wheel of Yoga, 123 Bear Road, Brighton, East Sussex BN2. Tel: (Editorial) 01273 698560

Resurgence Ford House, Hartland, Bideford, Devon EX39. Tel: 01237 441293 ed@resurge.demon.co.uk subs.resurge@virgin.net

Tricycle: The Buddhist Review Sharpham Coach Yard, Ashprington, Totnes, Devon TQ9. Tel: 01803 732082 buddhist.publishing@dial.pipex.com

Kindred Spirit Quarterly Foxhole, Dartington, Totnes, Devon TQ9. Tel: 01803 866686 kindred@spirit.co.uk

Parabola PO Box 3000, Denville, New Jersey 0783, USA www.parabola.org

OPEN CENTRES

Open Centres are various groups who are concerned with meditation, movement, healing, spirituality awareness and inter-faith work. They include but are not limited to yoga practices and retreats. They are, in essence, centred in spirituality and healing within the context of mind-body-spirit. The organisation which helps to link them together in common interest is called, simply, **Open Centres**.

Open Centres Avrils Farm, Lower Stanton St Quintin, Chippenham, Wiltshire SN14. Tel: 01249 720202 Open Centres publishes a bi-annual non-profit-making newsletter which links all the centres and people who share the same aims. The newsletter includes a directory listing groups around the country. These groups are involved in various activities and these often include yoga. One of the places may be near you. Here are a few examples:

The Abbey Sutton Courtney, Abingdon, Oxon OX14. Tel: 01235 847401

Amrit Hermitage Helland Cottage, Ladock, Cornwall TR2. Tel: 01726 883811

The Barn Lower Sharpham, Ashprington, Devon TQ9. Tel: 01803 732661

Beacon Centre Cutteridge Farm, Whitestone, Exeter EX4. Tel: 01392 81203

Beech Lawn Beech Grove, Mayford, Woking, Surrey GU22. Tel: 01483 747519

Bournemouth Centre C.M. 26 Sea Road, Boscombe, Bournemouth. Tel: 01202 36354

Bridge Trust W. Williamston, Back Cottage, Kilgetty SA68.
Caer Rosemerryn, Lamorna, Penzance, Cornwall TR19. Tel: 01773 672530
Centre of New Directions White Lodge, Stockland Green Road, Speldnurst, Kent TN3
Centre of Unity 6 Kings Grange, 46 West Cliff Road, Bournemouth, Dorset BH4
The Coach House Kilmuir, N. Kessock, Inverness IV1
Centre of Truth Suite 4, Carlton Chamber, 5 Station Road, Shortlands, Kent BR2
Coombe Quarr Coombe Hill, Keinton Mandeville, Somerset TA1. Tel: 01458 223215
Croydon Healing Centre 16 Bisdenden Road, Croydon, Surrey CR0. Tel: 020 8688 1856
Easter Centre 16 Bury Road, Hengrave, Bury St Edmunds, Suffolk IP28. Tel: 01284 704881
Ellbridge Broadhempston, Totnes, Devon TQ9. Tel: 01803 813015
Flint House 41 High Street, Lewes, East Sussex BN7 2LU. Tel: 01273 473388
Gaia House Woodland Road, Denbury, Devon TQ12 6DY. Tel: 01803 813188
The Grange Ellsmere, Shropshire SY1 9DE. Tel: 01691 623495
Hertfordshire Holistic Health Centre. Tel: 01707 24631
Kirkby Fleetham Hall Kirkby Fleetham, North Yorkshire GL7 0SU. Tel: 01609 748711
Middle Piccadilly Holwell, Sherbourne, Dorset. Tel: 01963 23468

SELECTED YOGA WEBSITES

There are more than five million documents about yoga on the web, and many give excellent information about yoga systems and the history of yoga as well as teachings about the spirituality aspects of this ancient form of healing and well-being.

Here are just a few titles or names that you might find interesting to put into your search engine:

Yoga Directory A good basic directory for many yoga links.

Yoga Meditation of the Himalayan Tradition Swami Jnaneshvara Bharati provides clear and interesting explanations of meditation, yoga, Vedanta, and internal tantra.

Yoga Science Evolution A resource with research by Swami Sannyasin Atmabhakta which includes articles by Paramhansa Satyananda Saraswati.

Yoga Tantra Veda The Yoga Tantra Veda site is very popular. Good information for downloading and very creative. Find out about the Bihar School of Yoga.

Yoga Research & Education Centre Established a number of years ago by Georg Feuerstein, a leading scholar of yoga. He has written over 30 books and this site is dedicated to preserving the traditional teachings of yoga. This is one of the more informative yoga sites on the web.

The following is a selection of websites we found interesting. From these you will discover endless links to other sites. Good searching!

www.retreatsonline.com/guide/yoga.htm

www.yogadirectory.com/Retreats

www.yoga.greatxscapes.net

www.yogacruise.com

www.londonyoga.com
www.yoga4health.biz/london.asp
www.triyoga.co.uk
www.yogaweekends.co.uk
www.yogawholesale.com
www.hoho.co.uk
www.yogaclass.net
www.places-to-be.com
www.bwy.com
www.celestopea.com/links/yoga.html
www.lovegrove.co.uk
www.ashtanga.com
www.bksiyta.co.uk
www.e-england.co.uk/holistichealth-yoga/
www.yogamagazine.co.uk/
www.viniyogatrainings.org/public_html/uk_options.html
www.iyengar-yoga.com/Yoga_Centers/Europe/
    United_Kingdom/
www.travel-quest.co.uk
www.wavewalker.freeserve.co.uk/yoga.htm
www.bksiyengar.com/teacherdir/UK.htm
www.viniyogatrainings.org/public_html/ph.html
www.iyta.org/TeachersDirectory/England.php
www.nirvichar.org/related_pages_list.html
www.lifefoundation.org.uk